P9-DHF-318

Ancient Civilizations

myWorld
INTERACTIVE
Active Journal

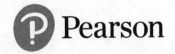 **Pearson**

Boston, Massachusetts   Chandler, Arizona
Glenview, Illinois   New York, New York

ISBN-13: 978-0-32-895881-8
ISBN-10: 0-32-895881-6

12 19

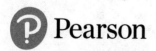

CONTENTS

CONTENTS

Topic 3
Ancient Egypt and Kush (3000 BCE–600 BCE)

Topic 4
Early Civilizations of India (3100 BCE–540 CE)

CONTENTS

Topic 5
Early Civilizations of China (1700 BCE–220 CE)

Topic 6
Ancient Greece (2000 BCE—300 BCE)

CONTENTS

Topic 7
The Roman Republic (800 BCE–30 BCE)

Topic 8
The Roman and Byzantine Empires (30 BCE—1453 CE)

CONTENTS

Origins of Civilization Preview

Essential Question How much does geography shape people's lives?

Before you begin this topic, think about the Essential Question by completing the following activity.

1. List the geographical features of your hometown. Describe any that influence how people live in your region.

2. Preview the topic by skimming lesson titles, headings, and graphics. Then study this list of the developments that took place in prehistoric times. How does each relate to geography?

humans domesticate animals   sea levels rise

the first cities appear   rivers deposit fertile soil

societies become more complex   sea levels drop during Ice Age

Timeline Skills

As you read, write and/or draw at least three events from the topic. Draw a line from each event to its correct position on the timeline.

| 2 million years ago | 300,000 years ago | 200,000 years ago | 100,000 years ago |

Map Skills

Using maps throughout the topic, label the outline map with the places listed.

Gulf of Aden   Red Sea   Lake Victoria

Ethiopia   Kenya   Tanzania

Olduvai Gorge   Indian Ocean   Hadar

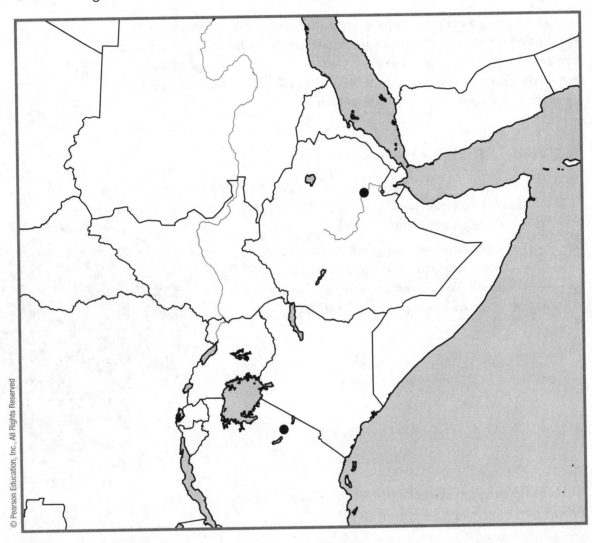

| 20,000 years ago | 15,000 years ago | 10,000 years ago | 5,000 years ago |

Quest
Project-Based Learning Inquiry

Design a Village

In this Quest, you will design a village that might have been built in Neolithic times. You will gather information about how early villagers lived by examining sources in your text and by conducting your own research. Then, you will design a Neolithic village and present your design to the class in an oral presentation.

1 Ask Questions (See Student Text, page 6)

As you begin your Quest, keep in mind the Guiding Question: **What was it like to live in an ancient village?** and the Essential Question: **How much does geography shape people's lives?**

What other questions do you need to ask in order to answer these questions? Consider the following aspects of life in prehistoric times. Two questions are filled in for you. Add at least two questions for each category.

Theme Location and Climate

Sample questions:

How did climate affect where people lived?

How did people protect themselves from harsh climates?

Theme Archaeology

Theme Social Organization

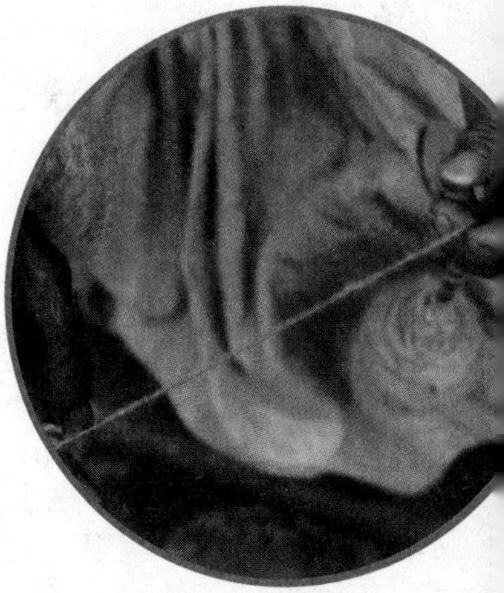

Theme Agriculture

Theme Building

Theme My Additional Questions

👆 INTERACTIVE

For extra help with Step 1, review the
21st Century Tutorial: **Ask Questions**.

② Investigate

As you read about the origins of civilization, collect five connections from your text to help you answer the Guiding Question. Three connections are already chosen for you.

Connect to Location

Lesson 3 When Did People Start to Farm?

Here's a connection! Look at the picture of a Neolithic settlement in Ireland in your text, and notice the settlement's location. What information does it give you about prehistoric life?

Why would people have chosen this spot to create a settlement in Neolithic times?

Connect to the Design of a Neolithic Village

Lesson 4 In-Text Primary Source The Houses of Çatalhöyük

Here's a connection! What does this Primary Source reveal about how the design of Çatalhöyük reflected villagers' priorities?

Why do you think the houses described in the Primary Source were packed so closely together, with no entrances at ground level?

Connect to Neolithic Shelters

Lesson 4 How Did the First Cities Begin?

What does the photo from your text show about how some ancient villagers built their shelters?

Why do you think these shelters are round?

7

It's Your Turn! **Find two more connections. Fill in the title of your connections, then answer the questions. Connections may be images, primary sources, maps, or text.**

Your Choice | Connect to

Location in text

What is the main idea of this connection?

What does it tell you about what it was like to live in an ancient village?

Your Choice | Connect to

Location in text

What is the main idea of this connection?

What does it tell you about what it was like to live in an ancient village?

③ Conduct Research (See Student Text, page 44)

Use the ideas in the Connections to further explore the subject of Neolithic villages. Find more sources about the subject.

Be sure to find valid sources and take good notes so you can properly cite your sources. Record key information and brainstorm ways to enhance your points with visuals. Then, form teams based on your teacher's instructions. Meet to decide who will take on each role. Write who will do what in the chart below.

Role	Team Member
Research life during the Neolithic Era	
Research Neolithic village sites	
Collect photos of reconstructions and sites	
Create a plan and drawing of your village	
Present your village to the class	

INTERACTIVE

For extra help, review the 21st Century Tutorials: **Work in Teams, Search for Information on the Internet,** and **Avoid Plagiarism**.

4 Design Your Village (See Student Text, page 44)

Now it's time to apply your research into Neolithic village sites and use that information to create your own Neolithic village.

1. **List Village Features** You have gathered information about Neolithic villages and looked at photographs and reconstructions of village sites. Make a list of the features that your village should have, taking into consideration factors such as local climate, food sources, defense against animals and enemies, and building materials.

Features

2. **Meet with Your Team** Meet with your team to discuss the images of Neolithic sites and other information that you have found. Compare information about the various village sites and discuss how these villages differed from one another, as well as the features they have in common.

3. **Make a List of Essential Features** After your discussion, make a list of the essential features that your village should have.

4. **Create and Present Your Design** Create a rough draft of the plan of the village. Discuss the plan with members of your team and suggest improvements. You may need to follow this process several times before presenting the finished designs.

5. **Reflect on the Quest** Think about your experience completing this topic's Quest. What did you learn about Neolithic life and the villages that were built during this period? What questions do you still have about the Neolithic world? How will you answer them?

Reflections

👆 **INTERACTIVE**

For extra help, review the 21st Century Tutorial: **Give an Effective Presentation**.

Take Notes

Literacy Skills: Main Idea and Details Use what you have read to complete the table. In each space, write one main idea and two details. The first one has been completed for you.

Studying Early Humans	Where Did Human Ancestors Live?	How Did Hunter-Gatherers Live?
Main Idea: Archaeologists use different methods for determining the ages of prehistoric objects.	**Main Idea:**	**Main Idea:**
Details: lower layers of soil are older; radioactive dating tells when an object was formed	**Details:**	**Details:**

> 👆 **INTERACTIVE**
>
> For extra help, review the 21st Century Tutorial: **Identify Main Ideas and Details**.

Practice Vocabulary

Word Map Study the word map for the word *artifact*. Characteristics are words or phrases that relate to the word in the center of the word map. Non-characteristics are words and phrases not associated with the word. Use the blank word map to explore the meaning of the word *culture*. Then make word maps of your own for these words: *anthropology, archaeologist, prehistory, fossil, geologist, technology,* and *hunter-gatherer*.

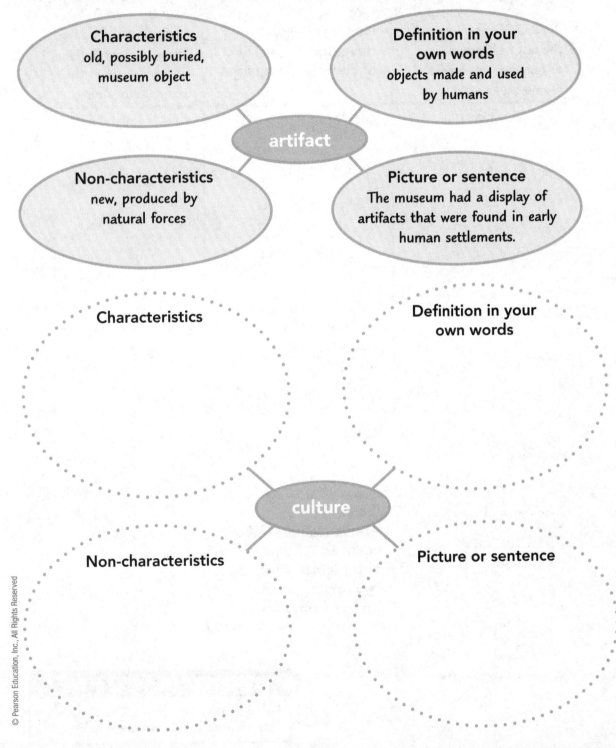

Characteristics
old, possibly buried, museum object

Definition in your own words
objects made and used by humans

artifact

Non-characteristics
new, produced by natural forces

Picture or sentence
The museum had a display of artifacts that were found in early human settlements.

Characteristics

Definition in your own words

culture

Non-characteristics

Picture or sentence

Take Notes

Literacy Skills: Analyze Cause and Effect Use what you have read to complete the organizer. For each event, write the cause in the box to the left and the effect in the box to the right. The first one has been completed for you.

Cause	Event	Effect
200,000 years ago, the last new group of humans appeared: Homo sapiens.	Homo sapiens developed the skill of complex language.	Language skills gave these modern humans an advantage in the struggle to survive.
	Glaciers form.	
	Sea levels drop, exposing "land bridges."	
	About 15,000–18,000 years ago, humans enter North America by crossing a land bridge from Asia.	

INTERACTIVE

For extra help, review the 21st Century Tutorial: **Analyze Cause and Effect**.

Practice Vocabulary

Vocabulary Quiz Show Some quiz shows ask a question and expect the contestant to give the answer. In other shows, the contestant is given an answer and must supply the question. If the blank is in the Question column, write the question that would result in the answer in the Answer column. If the question is supplied, write the answer.

Question

1. What happens when people leave their homeland to live elsewhere?

2. [blank]

3. What do you call it when you change your way of life to suit a new environment?

Answer

1. [blank]

2. environment

3. [blank]

Take Notes

Literacy Skills: Sequence Use what you have read to complete the flowcharts to show the sequence of events. The first flowchart has been completed for you.

Humans live as hunter-gatherers.

↓

As Ice Age ends, some animals and plants cannot adapt.

↓

People search for new sources of food.

↓

Some people begin to depend on fishing.

Hunter-gatherers develop language.

↓

`..................................................`

↓

Other animals are domesticated and herded.

↓

Grains become a food source.

↓

Over time, domesticated plants produce more food.

↓

`..................................................`

↓

More efficient metal tools are developed.

↓

`..................................................`

INTERACTIVE

For extra help, review the 21st Century Tutorial: **Sequence**.

Practice Vocabulary

Sentence Builder Finish the sentences below with a key term from this section. You may have to change the form of the words to complete the sentences.

Word Bank

animism   nomad   revolution

domesticate   populate

1. Due to centuries of migrations, there were few places on Earth that humans did not

   ....

2. The adoption of farming led to so many changes that it has been called a(n)

   ....

3. The wolf was one of the first animals that humans were able to

   ....

4. The belief that the natural world is full of spirits is known as

   ....

5. A person with no permanent home who moves from place to place is known as a(n)

   ....

Quick Activity Explore Cave Paintings

With a partner or small group, study these prehistoric paintings.

Team Challenge! With your partner or group, answer these questions: What colors did the artists use? Why? What kinds of animals, people, or activities are shown in the paintings? What was important to the people who created these paintings? How do you know? Why do you think the artists created these paintings? Share your answers orally with the class.

Take Notes

Literacy Skills: Analyze Cause and Effect Use what you have read to complete the organizer. For each event, write the cause in the box to the left and the effect in the box to the right. The first one has been completed for you.

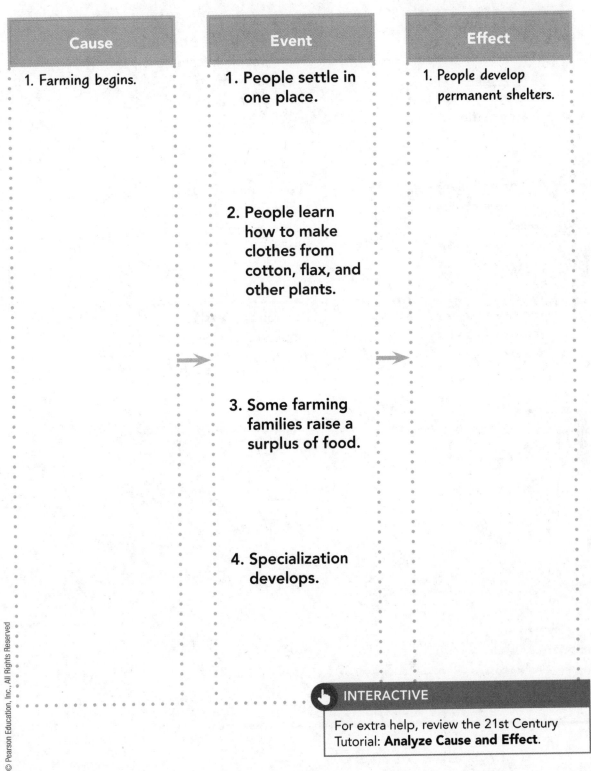

Cause	Event	Effect
1. Farming begins.	1. People settle in one place.	1. People develop permanent shelters.
	2. People learn how to make clothes from cotton, flax, and other plants.	
	3. Some farming families raise a surplus of food.	
	4. Specialization develops.	

👆 **INTERACTIVE**

For extra help, review the 21st Century Tutorial: **Analyze Cause and Effect**.

Practice Vocabulary

Matching Logic Using your knowledge of the underlined vocabulary words, draw a line from each sentence in Column 1 to match it with the sentence in Column 2 to which it logically belongs.

Column 1	Column 2
1. The villagers traded their <u>surplus</u> crops for pottery made in a nearby settlement.	Some people became skilled at weaving, pottery, or toolmaking.
2. <u>Specialization</u> led to a more complex society and an increase in trade.	The community had a system to produce and distribute goods and services.
3. The city of Uruk had a complex <u>economy</u>.	The good harvest supplied them with more than they could eat.

Quick Activity Explore Ancient Innovations

In prehistoric times, people developed new tools and practices that changed societies by increasing the population and improving the standard of living. What innovations do you see in the painting? Write you ideas in the space below.

My Ideas

Team Challenge! With a partner discuss the effect that one of the following innovations would have had on society: domestication of animals and plants; the ability to make tools; the ability to create art and music. Compare your ideas with classmates who discussed the same innovation.

Take Notes

Literacy Skills: Summarize Use what you have read to complete the flowcharts. Write a summary for each set of facts. The first flowchart has been completed for you.

As farming spread, settlements developed.

As settlements grew in size, specialization helped create complex societies.

↓

Summary: Farming led to the development of complex societies.

Governments managed society's resources.

Governments also formed and trained armies to defend society from attack.

↓

Summary:

The highest social class in most early societies was made up of priests and rulers.

Rulers of early civilizations claimed that their right to rule came from the gods.

↓

Summary:

 INTERACTIVE

For extra help, review the 21st Century Tutorial: **Summarize**.

Practice Vocabulary

Words in Context For each question below, write an answer that shows your understanding of the boldfaced vocabulary term.

1. Why did different **social classes** emerge in the early cities?

2. What **resources** were important to farmers?

3. What are some characteristics of **civilization**?

4. What were some features of **religion** in early civilizations?

Origins of Civilization

Take Notes

Literacy Skills: Use Evidence Use what you have read to complete the table. On each row, provide either evidence or a conclusion, based on your reading of the text. The first row has been done for you.

Evidence	Conclusion
Mesoamerica had rich soils in the uplands and lowland forests that provided resources.	Mesoamerica had the soils and resources to support the development of civilization.
	The Maya carefully managed their resources.
The Maya developed writing and made important discoveries in astronomy and mathematics.	
	Priests and kings were very powerful in Maya society.

INTERACTIVE

For extra help, review the 21st Century Tutorial: **Support Ideas With Evidence**.

Practice Vocabulary

True or False? Decide whether each statement below is true or false. Circle T or F, and then explain your answer. Be sure to include the underlined vocabulary word in your explanation. The first one is done for you.

1. **T / F** Rain fell heavily and flooded the land during the long <u>drought</u>.
   False; A <u>drought</u> is a dry period.

2. **T / F** The <u>quetzal</u> was a kind of mountain lion with black fur.

3. **T / F** Mayan <u>hieroglyphics</u> represented words, ideas, or sounds.

4. **T / F** The Maya built <u>observatories</u> to study the frequency of the tides.

5. **T / F** The Maya made weapons out of <u>obsidian</u>, a volcanic glass.

Writing Workshop Narrative Essay

Suppose you are visiting three different periods in the distant past to observe three different people: a hunter-gatherer, a herder, and a farmer. You will write a narrative essay describing the people you met and a few events in their lives. Although this assignment involves creative imagination, you should base the details and events on facts in the topic.

Lessons 1–3 Writing Task: Introduce Characters
(See Student Text, pages 12, 19, and 26)

Imagine how each character's life was shaped by his or her environment, way of life, and the time in which he or she lived. Write your ideas in the chart.

Character	Details
Hunter-gatherer	
Herder	
Farmer	

Lesson 4 Writing Task: Organize Sequence of Events
(See Student Text, page 32)

For each character, list the sequence of events you will include in your essay.

Character	Events
Hunter-gatherer	
Herder	
Farmer	

Lesson 5 Writing Task: Use Descriptive Details and Sensory Language
(See Student Text, page 37)

Imagine the sights, sounds, and tasks that would have been a familiar part of each character's world. Make a list of descriptive phases and adjectives that you can use for each character.

Character	Descriptive Details and Sensory Language
Hunter-gatherer	
Herder	
Farmer	

Lesson 6 Writing Task: Use Narrative Techniques
(See Student Text, page 43)

Write a few ideas about the narrative techniques you will use in your narrative essay. Remember, because you are, in fact, telling three stories, each should have a plot that rises to a climax, followed by a conclusion.

Writing Task (See Student Text, page 45)

Using the notes you have created on these pages, write a narrative essay about the lives of a hunter-gatherer, a herder, and a Neolithic farmer. Be sure to use evidence from your reading to support your response.

Essential Question **How do societies preserve order?**

Before you begin this topic, think about the Essential Question by answering the following questions.

1. What does *order* mean? In the space provided, write what order means for human societies in your own words. Then, write what it does not mean. You may list related words and phrases or write complete sentences.

What Order Means	What Order Does Not Mean

Timeline Skills

As you read, write and/or draw at least three events from the topic. Draw a line from each event to its correct position on the timeline.

4000 BCE	3000 BCE	2000 BCE

Map Skills

Using maps throughout the topic, label the outline map with the places listed. Then color in water, desert, mountains, and the Fertile Crescent.

Egypt	Canaan	Phoenicia	Mesopotamia
Persia	Babylon	Nineveh	Jerusalem
Persepolis	Tigris River	Euphrates River	

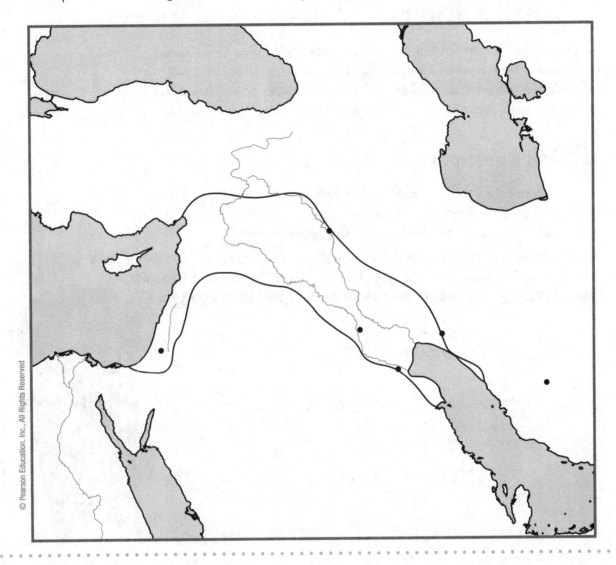

1000
BCE

1
CE

Quest

Discussion Inquiry

Debate Punishments for Crimes

Suppose you are an advisor to the President. You have been asked to research how best to keep order in our society. Then, you will participate in a civic discussion with other advisors about keeping order through appropriate punishments for crimes.

1 Ask Questions (See Student Text, page 50)

As you complete your Quest, keep in mind the Guiding Question: **Are harsh punishments necessary for a safe society?** and the Essential Question: **How do societies preserve order?**

What other questions do you need to ask in order to answer these questions? Consider the following themes. Two questions are filled in for you. Add at least two questions for each of the other categories.

Theme Government

  Sample questions:

Who ruled the civilizations of the Fertile Crescent?

What were their accomplishments?

Theme Economy and Trade

Theme Social Order

Theme Laws

Theme Religion

Theme My Additional Questions

INTERACTIVE

For extra help with Step 1, review the
21st Century Tutorial: **Ask Questions**.

2 Investigate

As you read about the civilizations and peoples of the Fertile Crescent, collect five connections from your text to help you answer the Guiding Question. Three connections are already chosen for you.

Connect to Mesopotamian Contracts

Primary Source Contracts in Ancient Mesopotamia
(See Student Text, page 58)

Here's a Connection! Read and think about written contracts in ancient Mesopotamia. How would agreements like these contribute to social order?

What do you think the punishment should be for breaking contracts such as these?

Connect to Social Order in Persia

Lesson 3 Cyrus the Great (See Student Text, page 68)

Here's another connection! Look at the biography of Cyrus the Great in your text and review what you've read about Cyrus and other Persian rulers. How did these rulers try to establish social order?

Do you think that punishments for crimes under Cyrus the Great's rule were harsh or mild? Explain your answer.

Connect to Teachings of Judaism

Lesson 6 Key Teachings of Judaism (See Student Text, page 86)

Here's another connection! Study the infographic on the key teachings of Judaism. What does this connection tell you about how the basic teachings of Judaism support social order?

How do you think people accused of wrongdoing were treated under Judaism?

It's Your Turn! Find two more connections. Fill in the title of your connections, then answer the questions. Connections may be images, primary sources, maps, or text.

Your Choice | Connect to

Location in text

What is the main idea of this connection?

What does it tell you about social order and justice in the Fertile Crescent?

Your Choice | Connect to

Location in text

What is the main idea of this connection?

What does it tell you about social order and justice in the Fertile Crescent?

③ Examine Sources (See Student Text, page 98)

One way societies create order is for citizens to know that there are possible punishments for their crimes. After a person has been convicted of a crime, judges today decide how harsh or mild the punishment should be. Some crimes have mandatory, or required, minimum sentences, however. Many lawmakers believe that people will stop committing crimes only if they are harshly punished.

Examine the primary and secondary sources provided online or from your teacher. Fill in the chart to show how these sources provide further information about whether harsh punishments are necessary for a safe society.

Are Harsh Punishments Necessary for a Safe Society?	
Source	**Yes or No? Why?**
J. Randy Forbes Testimony	
Sally Quillian Yates Testimony	
Mark Mauer Testimony	
"Mandatory Minimum Sentences"	

👆 **INTERACTIVE**

For extra help with Step 1, review the 21st Century Tutorials: **Analyze Primary and Secondary Sources** and **Evaluate Existing Arguments**.

Quest FINDINGS

4 Discuss! (See Student Text, page 98)

Now that you have collected clues and explored documents about harsh punishments, you are ready to discuss with your fellow advisors the Guiding Question: **Are harsh punishments necessary for a safe society?**

You will work with a partner in a small group of advisors. Try to reach consensus, a situation in which everyone is in agreement, on the question. Can you do it?

1. **Prepare your Arguments** You will be assigned a position on the question, either YES or NO.

   My position:

   Work with your partner to review your Quest notes from the Quest Connections and Quest Sources.

   • If you were assigned YES, agree with your partner on what you think were the strongest arguments from Forbes and Yates.

   • If you were assigned NO, agree on what you think were the strongest arguments from Mauer, Bernick, and Larkin.

2. **Present Your Position** Those assigned YES will present their arguments and evidence first. As you listen, ask clarifying questions to gain information and understanding.

What is a Clarifying Question?	
These types of questions do not judge the person talking. They are only for the listener to be clear on what he or she is hearing.	
Example: Can you tell me more about that?	Example: You said [x]. Am I getting that right?

👆 **INTERACTIVE**

For extra help with Step 4, review the 21st Century Tutorial: **Participate in a Discussion or Debate.**

While the opposite side speaks, take notes on what you hear in the space below.

3. **Switch!** Now NO and YES will switch sides. If you argued YES before, now you will argue NO. Work with your same partner and use your notes. Add any arguments and evidence from the clues and sources. Those *now* arguing YES go first.

When both sides have finished, answer the following:

Before I started this discussion with my fellow advisors, my opinion was that	*After* I started this discussion with my fellow advisors, my opinion was that
_____harsh punishments are necessary. _____harsh punishments are not necessary.	_____harsh punishments are necessary. _____harsh punishments are not necessary.

4. **Point of View** Do you all agree on the answer to the Guiding Question?

• _____ Yes

• _____ No

If not, on what points do you all agree?

Take Notes

Literacy Skills: Identify Main Ideas and Details Use what you have read to complete the tables. The column headings in the tables match the headings in your textbook. For each topic, write the main idea and some details that support it. The first one has been completed for you.

Agriculture in Mesopotamia	City-States of Sumer	Sumerian Religion
Main idea: Mesopotamia's rich soil allowed farmers to grow grains and vegetables and raise livestock. **Details:** • Tigris and Euphrates rivers carried silt across plains. • Sumerians used technology to irrigate crops. • Farmers developed a seed funnel to make planting faster and easier.	**Main idea:** **Details:**	**Main idea:** **Details:**

Sumerian Writing	Sumerian Government	Sumerian Achievements
Main idea: **Details:**	**Main idea:** **Details:**	**Main idea:** **Details:**

> INTERACTIVE
>
> For extra help, review the 21st Century Tutorial: **Identify Main Ideas and Details.**

Practice Vocabulary

Use a Word Bank Choose one word from the word bank to fill in each blank. When you have finished, you will have a short summary of important ideas from the section.

Word Bank

Fertile Crescent	bartering	Mesopotamia	polytheism
irrigate	ziggurats	city-states	cuneiform

The _____ is a region of the Middle East that

stretches from the Persian Gulf to the Mediterranean Sea. This region

includes _____, where several independent

states known as _____ developed. As these

communities developed, ancient Sumerians used technology to improve

agriculture. They learned how to _____, or

supply water to, their crops. They also exchanged goods without using

money in a trading system known as _____.

Sumerians practiced _____, or the belief in

more than one god. To honor their gods, they built pyramid-shaped

temples called _____. Sumerians also

developed a writing system in which scribes made wedge-shaped marks in

wet clay. This writing system was called _____.

Take Notes

Literacy Skills: Analyze Cause and Effect Use what you have read to complete the table. Write four causes and four effects of the listed event. The first one has been completed for you.

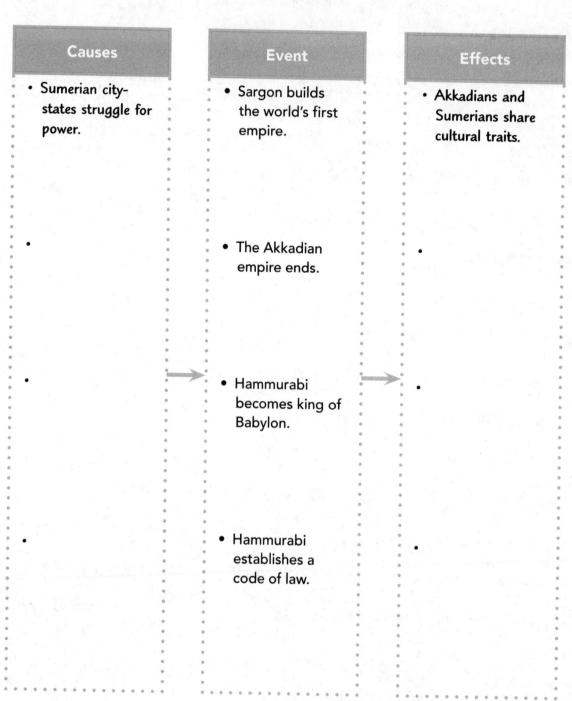

Causes	Event	Effects
• Sumerian city-states struggle for power.	• Sargon builds the world's first empire.	• Akkadians and Sumerians share cultural traits.
•	• The Akkadian empire ends.	•
•	• Hammurabi becomes king of Babylon.	•
•	• Hammurabi establishes a code of law.	•

INTERACTIVE

For extra help, review the 21st Century Tutorial: **Analyze Cause and Effect**.

Practice Vocabulary

Vocabulary Quiz Show Some quiz shows ask a question and expect the contestant to give the answer. In other shows, the contestant is given an answer and must supply the question. If the blank is in the Question column, write the question that would result in the answer in the Answer column. If the question is supplied, write the answer.

Question

1. What is the term for a state containing several countries or territories?

2. What phrase describes an idea or way of doing things that is common in a certain culture?

3.

4.

5. What is the word for an independent state that works with other states to achieve a shared military or political goal?

Answer

1.

2.

3. rule of law

4. Hammurabi's Code

5.

Quick Activity An Eye for an Eye?

You might have heard the phrase "an eye for an eye" used to justify punishments, revenge, and other harsh actions. The phrase is derived from Hammurabi's Code, a set of laws nearly 4,000 years old. The code was remarkable in its time for providing a written rule of law—but would you want the laws of ancient Babylon in effect today? Below are excerpts from Hammurabi's Code.

Hammurabi's Code	Level of Agreement
If any one bring an accusation of any crime before the elders, and does not prove what he has charged, he shall, if it be a capital offense charged, be put to death.	
If any one steal cattle or sheep, or an ass, or a pig or a goat, if it belong to a god or to the court, the thief shall pay thirtyfold therefor; if they belonged to a freed man of the king he shall pay tenfold; if the thief has nothing with which to pay he shall be put to death.	
If a man put out the eye of another man, his eye shall be put out.	
If he break another man's bone, his bone shall be broken.	
If during a quarrel one man strike another and wound him, then he shall swear, "I did not injure him wittingly," and pay the physicians.	

Team Challenge! Do these laws seem fair? Rank the degree to which you agree or disagree with each law: 1 = Strongly Agree, 2 = Agree, 3 = Unsure, 4 = Disagree, 5 = Strongly Disagree. Then, for each law, form groups of students with the same rankings. Discuss your reasoning and decide on one argument in favor of your position. Share your argument with the class.

Take Notes

Literacy Skills: Summarize Use what you have read to complete the table. Summarize the most important ideas from each section of the lesson in the appropriate column. The first one has been completed for you.

Section	Main Ideas
The Assyrian and Neo-Babylonian Empires	• The Assyrians fought against a steady stream of invaders, becoming fierce warriors with some of the earliest cavalry. • Nebuchadnezzar became king of Babylon, capturing Jerusalem and restoring Babylon to form the Neo-Babylonian empire.
Rise of the Persian Empire	
Persia's Government and Religion	
Arts of Mesopotamia	

Summary Statement:

 INTERACTIVE

For extra help, review the 21st Century Tutorial: **Summarize**.

Practice Vocabulary

Matching Logic Using your knowledge of the underlined vocabulary words, draw a line from each sentence in Column 1 to match it with the sentence in Column 2 to which it logically belongs.

Column 1	Column 2
1. The Assyrian army relied on its <u>cavalry</u> to defend and expand its empire.	Professional soldiers devoted to service protected the Persian Empire.
2. Cyrus the Great maintained a powerful <u>standing army</u>.	Darius introduced the use of gold coins as a medium of exchange.
3. Under Darius, the Persian empire used <u>tribute</u> money to fund great public works projects.	Soldiers rode into battle mounted on horses.
4. The Persian economy benefited from having a common <u>currency</u>.	Hammurabi's Code appears carved in stone beneath a relief showing Hammurabi and the Babylonian god Shamash.
5. Ancient Sumerians carved relief sculptures on <u>stele</u>.	Conquered peoples paid money to the emperor based on their wealth.

Take Notes

Literacy Skills: Summarize Use what you have read to complete the table. For each section in the lesson, write three sentences that summarize the section. Remember that a summary restates the most important information and ideas. The first one has been completed for you.

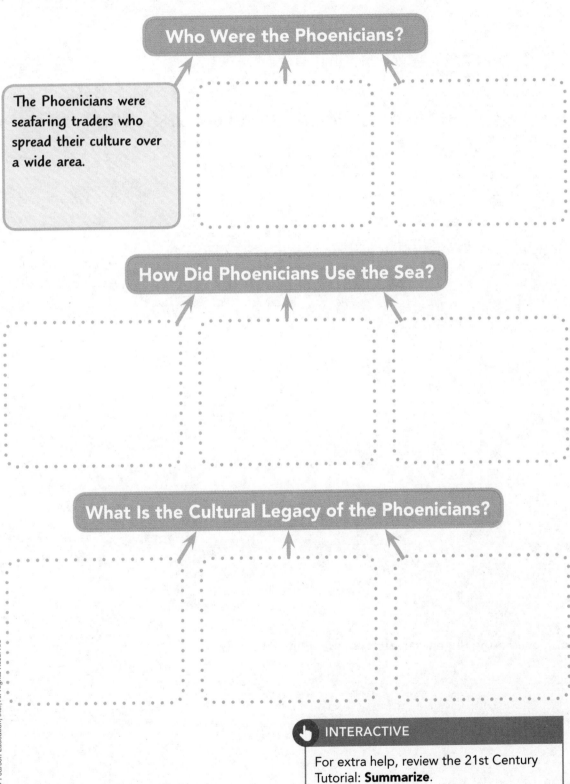

Who Were the Phoenicians?

The Phoenicians were seafaring traders who spread their culture over a wide area.

How Did Phoenicians Use the Sea?

What Is the Cultural Legacy of the Phoenicians?

👆 **INTERACTIVE**

For extra help, review the 21st Century Tutorial: **Summarize**.

Practice Vocabulary

Words in Context For each question below, write an answer that shows your understanding of the boldfaced vocabulary term.

1. Why did the Phoenician traders bring back so many **imports**?

2. What articles did Phoenician traders send as **exports** to other regions?

3. How did Phoenician sailors become experts in **navigation**?

4. How did Phoenician trading stations become **colonies**?

5. How did **cultural diffusion** help preserve the legacy of the Phoenicians?

6. How did the Phoenician **alphabet** simplify writing?

Quick Activity The Power of Invention

With a partner or small group, discuss the ways in which the invention of the wheel in ancient Mesopotamia impacted the peoples who lived there as well as later societies. Then make a list in the space below of other inventions that originated in the Fertile Crescent. Circle those that had an impact on later societies.

Team Challenge! Many societies have benefited from tools, weapons, medical advances, and other innovations. Consider what inventions you enjoy and depend on. Using three index cards or sticky notes, write three inventions that you consider the most important to your life. Post the notes on a class message board. As a class, identify the items that appear most often. Vote on which ones have had the most impact on our society or on humanity in general. Form groups according to votes, discuss your reasoning, and then debate with the other groups.

Take Notes

Literacy Skills: Summarize Use what you have read to complete the table. Summarize in the appropriate column each section's most important information. The first one has been completed for you. Then, use those ideas to write a summary statement.

Section	Main Ideas
The Early Israelites	• belief in one God • emphasis on ethics • The Torah tells the story of the origins of Judaism. • God makes a covenant with Abraham to lead his people to the Promised Land.
The Exodus	
The Ten Commandments	
The Promised Land	

Summary Statement:

 INTERACTIVE

For extra help, review the 21st Century Tutorial: **Summarize**.

Practice Vocabulary

Use a Word Bank Choose one word from the word bank to fill in each blank. When you have finished, you will have a short summary of important ideas from the lesson.

Word Bank

commandments	covenant	ethics
Exodus	monotheism	Torah

Unlike many other religions that originated in the Fertile

Crescent, Judaism is a belief in only one God, which is known as

_____. The first five books of the Bible, called

the _____, tell how Judaism began. These

books describe how God told the Israelites to practice proper behavior,

or _____. The Torah tells that God made a

_____ with Abraham, whom Jews consider

to be the founder of their religion. According to the Bible, the Israelites

ended up in Egypt, where they became slaves. Moses became their

leader and helped them in an escape from slavery, in what is known as the

_____. The Bible describes how God told Moses

to give the Israelites a series of ten _____ to

teach them how to act toward God and toward other people.

Take Notes

Literacy Skills: Analyze Cause and Effect Use what you have read to complete the chart. In the Text column, you will see a type of Jewish religious text, including the three sections of the Hebrew Bible. In the Effect column, write ways in which that body of texts has affected Jewish beliefs. The first one has been completed for you.

Text	Effect on Jewish Beliefs
The Torah	contains many of the rules and laws by which the Jewish people live
The Prophets	
The Writings	
Talmud/Commentaries	

INTERACTIVE

For extra help, review the 21st Century Tutorial: **Analyze Cause and Effect.**

Practice Vocabulary

Vocabulary Quiz Show Some quiz shows ask a question and expect the contestant to give the answer. In other shows, the contestant is given an answer and must supply the question. If the blank is in the Question column, write the question that would result in the answer in the Answer column. If the question is supplied, write the answer.

Question

1.

2. Who is a person chosen by God to bring messages to the people?

3.

4. What is the name of the collection of teachings and commentaries about the Bible and Jewish law?

5.

6.

Answer

1. justice

2.

3. rabbi

4.

5. righteousness

6. Sabbath

Take Notes

Literacy Skills: Sequence Use what you have read to complete the timeline. Record key events from the lesson in the appropriate space on the timeline. The first one has been completed for you.

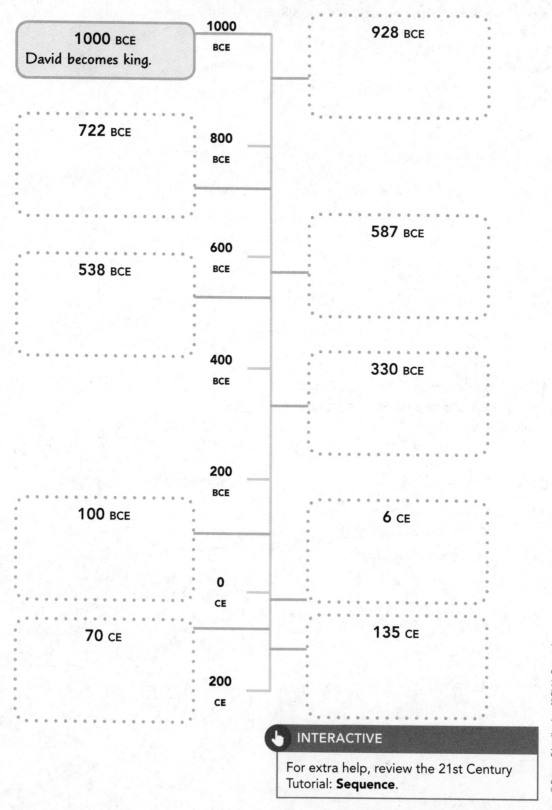

1000 BCE
David becomes king.

928 BCE

722 BCE

800 BCE

587 BCE

600 BCE

538 BCE

400 BCE

330 BCE

200 BCE

100 BCE

6 CE

0 CE

70 CE

135 CE

200 CE

INTERACTIVE

For extra help, review the 21st Century Tutorial: **Sequence**.

Practice Vocabulary

Words in Context For each question below, write an answer that shows your understanding of the boldfaced key term.

1. What is a **synagogue** used for?

2. What were the original causes of the **Diaspora**?

3. What did the Jews do when the king of the Persians, Cyrus the Great, ended the Babylonian **Exile**?

4. What role did **judges** play among the Israelites, according to the Bible?

Writing Workshop Narrative Essay

What was life like for people in ancient Mesopotamia? How did the environment affect the ways people lived? What technologies did they use to overcome challenges and solve problems? The prompts below will help walk you through the process of preparing to write your narrative essay about the life of someone living in ancient Mesopotamia.

Lessons 1 and 2 Writing Task: Introduce Characters
(See Student Text, pages 57 and 64)

Identify different groups of people who lived in ancient Mesopotamia. Then, circle one group about whom you want to write and imagine a character to represent them. Compose a sentence in which you describe your character's age, sex, and social class. Describe his or her profession and explain where and with whom your character probably lived. Brainstorm a name!

With which groups would your character interact? Write down three characters, identify their role in society, and explain what relationship they would have had with your character.

Lesson 3 Writing Task: Establish Setting (See Student Text, page 70)

Did your character live in Sumer, in Akkadia, in Babylon, or in Assyria? Did he or she live in a city, such as Ur, or outside of a city? Where would your character have spent the most time—on a farm, in a palace, in a temple, at a market, or in battle? Write two to three sentences to describe the setting of your narrative essay.

Lessons 4 and 5 Writing Task: Organize Sequence of Events
(See Student Text, pages 76 and 81)

What would life be like for your character over the course of a day? What would he or she do? What other characters would he or she meet, where would he or she go, what work and what fun things might he or she do, and what challenges would he or she face? List a sequence of at least four events or activities for your character's day.

Lesson 6 Writing Task: Use Narrative Techniques (See Student Text, page 88)

Consider the mood and tone that you will use. You might write your narrative to be exciting, scary, funny, or dramatic and serious. Brainstorm what narrative techniques you can use to make your story interesting to read. Decide whether you will write in first or third person and whether you will write in past or present tense.

Lesson 7 Writing Task: Use Descriptive Details and Sensory Language
(See Student Text, page 96)

What people, plants, food and drink, music and sounds, weather, clothing, and tools or weapons might your character experience? What does he or she see, hear, feel, taste, and smell?

Writing Task (See Student Text, page 99)

Use your ideas to write a first draft for your essay. Ask yourself: Does the essay reflect what life might have been like for the character? Does it contain details about the setting? Does it show the effects of environment? Does it show how people use technology to solve problems? Revise your draft, being sure to use proper grammar and punctuation.

Essential Question **What makes a great leader?**

Before you begin this topic, think about the Essential Question by completing the following activity.

1. List three qualities of a great leader. Then, circle the one leadership quality that you think is the most important.

2. Preview the topic by skimming lesson titles, headings, and graphics. Then, place a check mark next to the qualities that you predict will be true about the leaders of ancient Egypt and Kush.

__ powerful   __ weak   __ concerned about the afterlife

__ wealthy   __ respected   __ uninterested in the arts

__ religious   __ monument builders

Timeline Skills

As you read, write and/or draw at least three events from the topic. Draw a line from each event to its position on the timeline.

4000 BCE	3000 BCE

Map Skills

Using maps throughout the topic, label the outline map with the places listed. Then color in water, desert, and areas of fertile land.

Western Desert   Eastern Desert   Lower Egypt   Upper Egypt

Africa   Asia   Sinai Peninsula   Red Sea

Nile River   Nile Delta   Mediterranean Sea   Kush

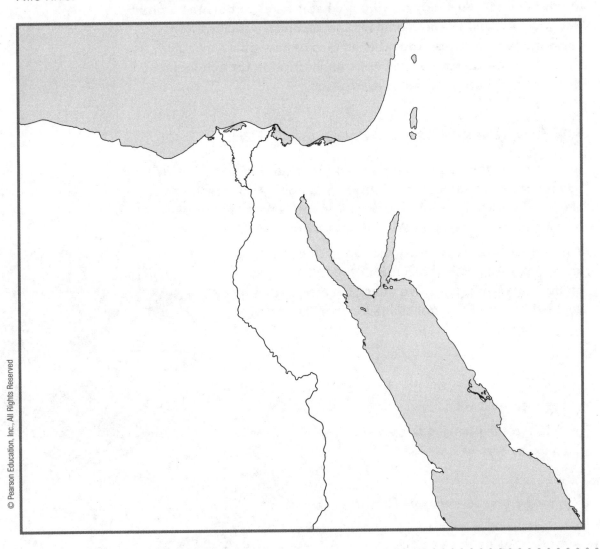

2000	1000	1
BCE	BCE	BCE

Quest
Document-Based Writing Inquiry

Become a Pharaoh-in-Training

On this Quest, you need to find out what it takes to become a great pharaoh. You will examine primary and secondary sources from ancient Egypt and Kush to find examples of how pharaohs ruled. At the end of the Quest, you will write an inscription for a monument that records your great deeds as pharaoh.

1 Ask Questions (See Student Text, page 104)

As you begin your Quest, keep in mind the Guiding Question: **What do you need to learn to become a great pharaoh?** Also, consider how ancient Egyptian pharaohs governed Egypt as part of your exploration of the Essential Question: **What makes a great leader?**

What other questions do you need to ask in order to answer these questions? Consider the following aspects of life in ancient Egypt. Two questions are filled in for you. Add at least two questions for each category.

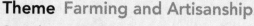
Theme Farming and Artisanship

Sample questions:

What role did farming and artisanship play in helping pharaohs become great?

How did pharaohs support farmers and artisans?

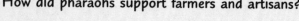
Theme Architecture and Building

Theme Science and Medicine

Theme Religion, Art, and Literature

Theme Trade and Warfare

Theme My Additional Questions

 INTERACTIVE

For extra help with Step 1, review the 21st Century Skills Tutorial: **Ask Questions**.

② Investigate

As you read about ancient Egypt and Kush, collect five connections from your text to help you answer the Guiding Question. Three connections are already chosen for you.

Connect to Egypt's Social Pyramid

Lesson 1 How Was Egyptian Society Organized?

(See Student Text, page 109)

Here's a connection! Look at the social pyramid diagram in your text. The pharaoh is at the top. What roles do people on the other levels fulfill? How do they support you, the pharaoh? What does this diagram tell you about being a great pharaoh?

How do you, as pharaoh, benefit the people?

Connect to The Victory of Ramses II

Primary Source The Victory of Ramses II (See Student Text, page 113)

Here's another connection! What does this primary source tell you about the power of a pharaoh in ancient Egypt? According to the poem, how does Ramses II prove his worthiness to be pharaoh?

What questions would you ask Ramses II if you could talk to him?

Connect to The Great Pyramid of Giza

Lesson 2 Architecture and Art (See Student Text, page 117)

What does this connection tell you about Egyptian society during the reign of Khufu? What does the pyramid say about Khufu as a pharaoh?

What were Egyptian pharaohs trying to accomplish by building pyramids?

It's Your Turn! Find two more connections. Fill in the title of your connections, then answer the questions. Connections may be images, primary sources, maps, or text.

Your Choice | Connect to

Location in text

What is the main idea of this connection?

What does it tell you about how you, as pharaoh, should use your power?

Your Choice | Connect to

Location in text

What is the main idea of this connection?

What does it tell you about how you, as pharaoh, should use your power?

③ Examine Primary Sources (See Student Text, page 128)

Examine the primary and secondary sources provided online or from your teacher. Fill in the chart to show how these sources provide further information about how to become a great pharaoh. The first one is completed for you.

Source	I am a great pharaoh because . . .
Hymn to the Nile	I fulfill all of my duties to worship the gods and keep them sending the flood waters to nourish the crops and feed the people.
Tomb of Tutankhamun	
Edwin Smith Surgical Papyrus	
Judgment of the Dead	
Luxury Products Imported by Ancient Egypt	

👆 INTERACTIVE

For extra help with Step 3, review the 21st Century Skills Tutorials: **Analyze Primary and Secondary Sources** and **Analyze Images**.

4 Write Your Monument Inscription (See Student Text, page 128)

Now it's time to put together all of the information you have gathered and use it to write your inscription.

1. **Prepare to Write** You have collected connections and explored primary and secondary sources that show how to be a great pharaoh. Look through your notes and decide which accomplishments you want to highlight in your monument inscription. Record them here.

Accomplishments

2. **Write a Draft** Using evidence from the clues you found and the documents you explored, write a draft of your inscription. Introduce yourself in character as pharaoh, then describe your accomplishments. Be sure to use vivid details that spring from evidence in the documents you've studied in this Quest.

3. **Share With a Partner** Exchange your draft with a partner. Tell your partner what you like about his or her draft, and suggest any improvements.

4. **Finalize Your Inscription** Revise your inscription. Correct any grammatical or spelling errors. Finally, make a sketch of your monument showing your inscription.

5. **Reflect on the Quest** Think about your experience completing this topic's Quest. What did you learn about ancient Egypt and its pharaohs? What questions do you still have about ancient Egypt? How will you answer them?

Reflections

👆 INTERACTIVE

For extra help with Step 4, review the 21st Century Skills Tutorial: **Write an Essay**.

Take Notes

Literacy Skills: Main Idea and Details Use what you have read to complete the table. In each space, write one main idea and two details. The first one has been completed for you.

The Nile River Valley	How Did Egyptian Civilization Develop?	The Kingdoms of Egypt
Main Idea: The Nile River strongly affected life in ancient Egypt.	**Main Idea:**	**Main Idea:**
Details: Strips of fertile land between deserts supported farming. Unpredictable flooding could lead to crop failure and widespread hunger.	**Details:**	**Details:**

How Was Egyptian Society Organized?	Egyptian Religion	Great Rulers
Main Idea:	**Main Idea:**	**Main Idea:**
Details:	**Details:**	**Details:**

👆 **INTERACTIVE**

For extra help, review the 21st Century Skills Tutorial: **Identify Main Ideas and Details.**

Practice Vocabulary

Word Map Study the word map for the word *cataract*. Characteristics are words or phrases that relate to the word in the center of the word map. Non-characteristics are words and phrases not associated with the word. Use the blank word map to explore the meaning of the word *pharaoh*. Then make word maps of your own for these words: *mummy, dynasty, bureaucracy, delta,* and *artisan*.

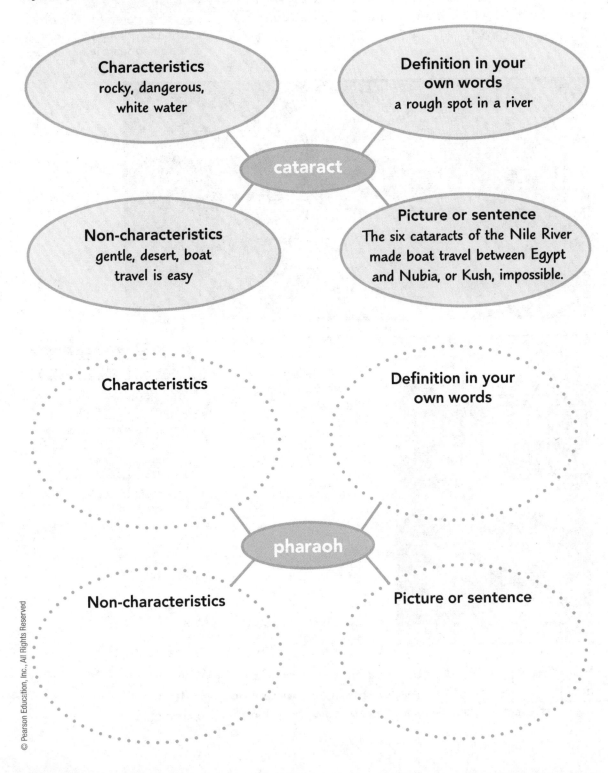

Characteristics
rocky, dangerous,
white water

**Definition in your
own words**
a rough spot in a river

cataract

Non-characteristics
gentle, desert, boat
travel is easy

Picture or sentence
The six cataracts of the Nile River
made boat travel between Egypt
and Nubia, or Kush, impossible.

Characteristics

**Definition in your
own words**

pharaoh

Non-characteristics

Picture or sentence

Quick Activity How Did Ancient Egyptians View Their Pharaohs?

Ancient Egypt is famous for the murals and sculptures that honor its pharaohs. In a small group, examine the images below. Think about why elaborate portrayals of Egyptian gods would be painted on the walls of pharaohs' tombs. What do you notice about the sculpture of the pharaoh that signifies his position in Egyptian society?

Did you know?

Horus, Egyptian god of the sky and of war, was also the god of kingship. Often, he is shown as a man with a falcon's head. Atum, god of creation, is considered the first of the Egyptian gods. He often appears in a blue headdress.

▲ This mural painting, from the tomb of Ramses I, depicts the pharaoh between the gods Horus and Atum.

Did you know?

The shepherd's crook and the ankh, a rounded cross, are symbols of the pharaoh. The crook signifies kingship. The ankh represents life, or creation.

◄ Pharaoh statue outside the Temple of Hatshepsut

Team Challenge! Imagine that you are visiting ancient Egypt. As a group, choose one of the images shown and write a postcard from the past, sharing your thoughts about how the pharaohs are depicted here.

Take Notes

Literacy Skills: Summarize Use what you have read to complete the table. In each space, summarize important ideas that you learned from the section, in your own words. Write your summaries in complete sentences. The first one has been completed for you.

Section	Summary
Writing and Literature	• Ancient Egyptians used hieroglyphics, which are symbols or drawings, to write. • Most Egyptians could not read or write hieroglyphics. Officials, called *scribes*, recorded information. Scribes wrote in ink on papyrus sheets. • Egyptians used hieroglyphics to write poems, stories, songs, histories, religious ideas, and other information.
Art and Architecture	• • •
Science and Mathematics	• • •

INTERACTIVE

For extra help, review the 21st Century Skills Tutorial: **Summarize**.

Practice Vocabulary

Sentence Revision Revise each sentence so that the underlined vocabulary word is used logically. Be sure not to change the vocabulary word. The first sentence is completed for you.

1. Ancient Egyptians used <u>hieroglyphics</u> to represent letters in a word.
   Ancient Egyptians used <u>hieroglyphics</u> to represent words or sounds.

2. Egyptians wrote in ink on a paper-like material called <u>papyrus</u>, made from trees.

3. During the Old Kingdom, large numbers of workers built massive <u>pyramids</u> to serve as palaces for pharaohs.

4. Skilled Egyptian artists made colossal <u>sculptures</u> of royal officials to stand outside their temples.

5. Egyptians learned a great deal about human <u>anatomy</u> from their work with engineers and used this knowledge to become skilled doctors and surgeons.

Quick Activity How Did They Do It?

With a partner or small group, examine this modern-day photo of the Great Pyramid of King Khufu at Giza.

Did you notice the stone blocks that were used to build the Great Pyramid? How did the ancient Egyptians move these massive blocks across the sand to the construction site? No one knows for sure, but the photo includes an important clue.

▲ Recreation of a wall painting showing the moving of a statue of a pharoah

Team Challenge! How do you think they did it? Draw or write your theory on a sheet of paper, then post your ideas in your classroom. Take a gallery walk to view everyone's ideas, then compare them to what the experts hypothesize by searching online.

Take Notes

Literacy Skills: Analyze Cause and Effect Use what you have read to complete the table. List appropriate causes from the lesson in the middle column and their effects in the right column. Be sure to record two cause-and-effect relationships for each section. The first one has been completed for you.

Section	Cause	Effect
Why Was Trade Important for Egypt and Kush?	Egypt wanted gold and other luxury items that it did not possess itself.	Egypt began trading its goods to Kush in exchange for gold, ivory, and ebony.
How Did Kush Develop?		
Kush and Egypt		
What Were Kush's Accomplishments?		

👆 **INTERACTIVE**

For extra help, review the 21st Century Skills Tutorial: **Analyze Cause and Effect**.

Practice Vocabulary

Matching Logic Using your knowledge of the underlined vocabulary words, draw a line from each sentence in Column 1 to match it with the sentence in Column 2 to which it logically belongs.

Column 1	Column 2
1. To obtain resources that it did not have, Egypt began engaging in <u>commerce</u> with nearby countries.	Scholars have yet to figure out the language recorded in this alphabet.
2. In addition to gold, Egyptians traded with Kush for <u>ebony</u> and <u>ivory</u>.	New Kingdom pharaohs signed peace treaties with former enemies, such as the Hittites, to promote trade.
3. As a result of increasing trade, Egypt and Kush developed a relationship of <u>interdependence</u>.	Closer economic ties led to an exchange of cultures and ideas.
4. Unlike ancient Egyptians, Kushites developed an alphabetic script called <u>Meroitic script</u>.	In return, Kush came to rely on Egyptian grain.

Writer's Workshop Explanatory Essay

As you read, build a response to this question: **How did geography affect the people of ancient Egypt and Kush?** The prompts below will walk you through the process.

Lesson 1 Writing Task: Develop a Clear Thesis (See Student Text, page 112)

Express in one sentence the most significant effects of the region's geography on ancient Egyptians. This will be your thesis statement for the explanatory essay that you will write at the end of the Topic.

After you read Lessons 2 and 3, re-read your thesis statement. Is it still valid? Does it need any revision to include the information you learned in Lessons 2 and 3? If so, write your revision here:

Lesson 2 Writing Task: Support Thesis With Details (See Student Text, page 119)

Refer to the statement you wrote in Lesson 1. What details from Lessons 1 and 2 support your point? Add details from Lesson 3 after you read the lesson.

Lesson 1	
Lesson 2	
Lesson 3	

Lesson 3 Writing Task: Organize Your Essay (See Student Text, page 126)

Make an outline of your essay. Start with an introduction, followed by three paragraphs that explain the effect of geography on ancient Egypt and Kush, and end with a conclusion. Use the chart below to help you.

Introduction Thesis	
Effect 1 Evidence	
Effect 2 Evidence	
Effect 3 Evidence	
Conclusion	

Writing Task (See Student Text, page 129)

Using the outline you created in Lesson 3, answer the following question in a five-paragraph explanatory essay: **How did geography affect the lives of ancient Egyptians and Nubians?**

As you write, consider using the following cause-and-effect signal words to transition between points: *because, consequently, therefore, for this reason*, and *as a result.*

75

Early Civilizations of India Preview

Essential Question **What makes a culture endure?**

Before you begin this topic, think about the Essential Question by answering the following question.

1. Culture includes art, music, literature, food, and dance. It also includes shared ideas about how to live, what to value, and religious beliefs. What would you like people to know about your own culture? Write three ideas below.

Timeline Skills

As you read, write and/or draw at least three events from the topic. Draw a line from each event to its correct position on the timeline.

3000 BCE	2500 BCE	2000 BCE	1500 BCE

Map Skills

Using maps throughout the topic, label the outline map with the places listed. Then, color the mountains, water, and the Indian subcontinent.

Indian Ocean   Indus River   Hindu Kush

Ganges River   Arabian Sea   Himalayas

Deccan Plateau   Bay of Bengal

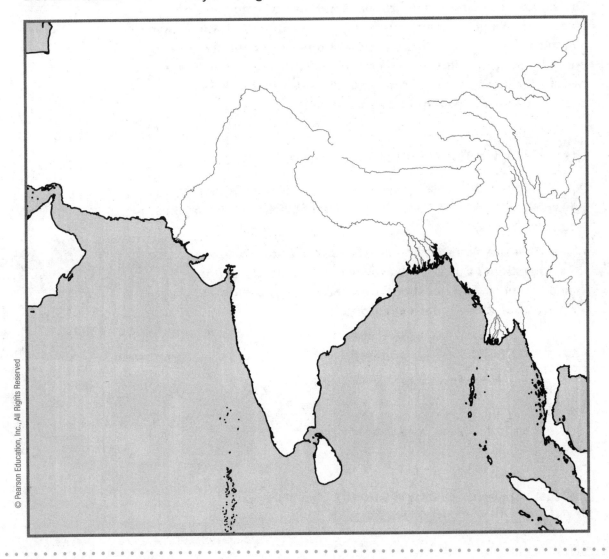

| 500 BCE | 1 CE | 500 CE |

Quest

A Trip Through India

On this Quest, you will need to find out how the influences of ancient India still endure in modern Indian culture. You will examine sources from ancient India and find examples of how they remain a part of modern culture. At the end of the Quest, you will create a travel brochure of some of the culturally and historically important sites that you would want to be sure to visit.

1 Ask Questions (See Student Text, page 134)

As you begin your Quest, keep in mind the Guiding Question: **Where should you visit?** and the Essential Question: **What makes a culture endure?**

What other questions do you need to ask in order to answer these questions? Consider the following aspects of culture in ancient India. Two questions are filled in for you. Add at least two questions in each category.

Theme Arts and Literature

Sample questions:

What ideas did people in ancient India portray in their art?

What were the main ideas in ancient Indian literature?

Theme Geography

Theme Religion

Theme Rulers and Warfare

Theme Achievements

Theme My Additional Questions

 INTERACTIVE

For extra help with Step 1, review the
21st Century Tutorial: **Ask Questions**.

 **CONNECTIONS**

2 Investigate

As you read about ancient India, collect five connections from your text to help you answer the Guiding Question. Three connections are already chosen for you.

Connect to the Buddha

Primary Source The Life or Legend of Gaudama (See Student Text, page 164)

Here's a connection! What did the Buddha learn from his meditation?

Why do you think Buddhism spread to other parts of the world and is still practiced today?

Connect to Asoka

Lesson 6 What Was Asoka's Legacy? (See Student Text, page 172)

Encouraged by Asoka's conversion to Buddhism, Buddhists spread the teachings of the Buddha to neighboring regions. What could visitors learn about Buddhism by visiting a monastery outside of India?

Based on the photo of the Sri Lankan monastery, how might the practice of Buddhism today be both similar and different from ancient times?

Connect to the Guptas

Lesson 7 What Was Gupta Culture Like? (See Student Text, page 176)

Here's another connection! Gupta culture was the golden age of India. What kinds of art were created during the Gupta reign?

How do you think this affects the culture of present-day India?

It's Your Turn! **Find two more connections. Fill in the title of your connections, then answer the questions. Connections may be images, primary sources, maps, or text.**

Your Choice | Connect to

Location

What is the main idea of this connection?

What does this tell you about how culture endures and where you should visit in India?

Your Choice | Connect to

Location

What is the main idea of this connection?

What does this tell you about how culture endures and where you should visit in India?

③ Conduct Research (See Student Text, page 180)

You will need to conduct research about places to visit and things to do in India. With your group, start by making a list of possible places that you may want to highlight in your brochure. You may continue your list on a separate sheet of paper. Refine your list as you learn more. Assign researchers for each location. Be sure to take good notes as you research and collect photos that you might want to use.

Places to Visit	Assigned to

👆 **INTERACTIVE**

For extra help with Step 3, review the 21st Century Tutorial: **Work in Teams**.

Quest FINDINGS

4 Create a Travel Brochure (See Student Text, page 180)

Once you have concluded your research, create a travel brochure that includes historical and cultural things to do and see in India. Your brochure should include specific information about each of the sites you'll visit. Be sure to include why the sites you have chosen are still relevant to the culture of present-day India.

Follow these steps to put together all of the information you have gathered and use it to create your brochure.

1. **Narrow Your Focus** You have collected connections and conducted research about places to visit that are of cultural and historical significance in India. Look through your notes, and decide with your group which places you will include and why.

2. **Write a Draft** Decide who in your group will be assigned to describe which place(s) and decide on the order in which to present the places selected. Then, write a rough draft describing each place and its significance. Assign someone in your group to write an introduction.

3. **Share with a Partner** Exchange your draft with other members of your group. Tell each other what you like about each draft and suggest improvements.

4. **Finalize Your Brochure** Correct any spelling or grammatical errors. Include photos with captions where they are relevant. Use technology to finalize and publish your brochure. Consider a layout and design that will be appealing and useful for your audience.

5. **Reflect on the Quest** Think about your experience completing this topic's Quest. What did you learn about ancient India and how its culture has endured into the present day? What questions do you still have about ancient India? How will you answer them?

Reflections

 INTERACTIVE

For extra help with Step 4, review the 21st Century Tutorial: **Publish Your Work**.

Take Notes

Literacy Skills: Identify Main Ideas and Details Use what you have read to complete the table. In each space, write one main idea and two details. The first one has been completed for you.

What Is the Indian Subcontinent?
Main Idea: The Indian subcontinent is set apart from the rest of the continent. **Details:** The Himalayas and the Hindu Kush separate the continent geographically. The climate of the subcontinent is influenced by the mountains to the north and the ocean to the south.

Indus Valley Civilization	What Mysteries Surround the Indus Valley Civilization?
Main Idea: Details:	Main Idea: Details:

INTERACTIVE

For extra help, review the 21st Century Tutorial: **Identify Main Ideas and Details**.

Practice Vocabulary

Use a Word Bank Choose one word from the word bank to fill in each blank. When you have finished, you will have a short summary of important ideas from the section.

Word Bank

granary   subcontinent   citadel

river system   monsoon

The Indus Valley Civilization formed on the Indian

[_____] around 7000 BCE. Geography was

very important to how the civilization developed. One important

geographic feature was the [_____]

that included the Indus River. Another was the summer

[_____] winds that brought rain, causing the

rivers to flood. This fertile land meant that there was enough food

to save some in a [_____], so everyone had

enough to eat. As the cities grew, each one protected itself with a

[_____].

Quick Activity Museum Gallery

Examine the artifacts shown. With a partner, select one artifact to focus on.

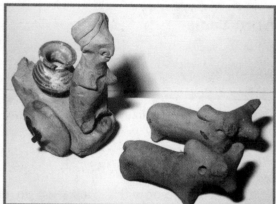

Team Challenge! Imagine that you and your partner are writing the description of your artifact for the museum exhibit. Write a short description of the artifact. Then, write what you think it tells us about life in the Indus Valley.

Take Notes

Literacy Skills: Summarize Use what you have read to complete the table. For each major topic in this section, write down 2–3 of the most important facts. Use your notes to write a summary of the section.

The Indo-Aryans	The Vedas	Caste

Summary:

INTERACTIVE

For extra help, review the 21st Century Tutorial: **Summarize**.

Practice Vocabulary

Sentence Builder Finish the sentences below with a key term from this section. You may have to change the form of the word(s) to complete the sentences.

Word Bank

Veda   caste

jati   varna

1. A fixed social class into which a person is born is called a

2. One of two social groupings that is based on one's skill is called

3. The sacred hymns written by the Indo-Aryans came to be known as

   the

4. One of two social groupings that is based on one's occupation is

   called

Take Notes

Literacy Skills: Sequencing Use what you have read to complete the sequence. In each space, write one main idea that traces the development of Hinduism in India.

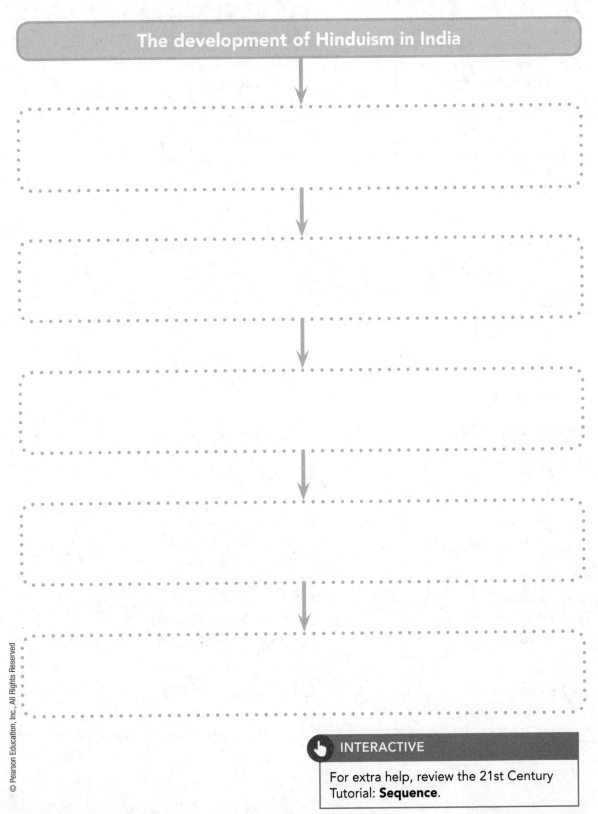

The development of Hinduism in India

INTERACTIVE

For extra help, review the 21st Century Tutorial: **Sequence**.

Practice Vocabulary

Matching Logic Using your knowledge of the underlined vocabulary words, draw a line from each sentence in Column 1 to match it with the sentence in Column 2 to which it logically belongs.

Column 1	Column 2
1. You must always follow your <u>dharma</u>.	These thinkers and teachers wanted to think and talk about religious ideas.
2. <u>Gurus</u> often left their homes to go live in the forest.	The soul is reborn in a new body.
3. The final goal of Hinduism is <u>moksha</u>.	Living things are never to be harmed.
4. When people die, they will most likely go through <u>reincarnation</u>.	Hinduism is flexible because all Gods are a form of this.
5. You must always follow the rule of <u>ahimsa</u>.	The goal is to live your life so you can return as something better.
6. All of your actions affect your <u>karma</u>.	When your soul is liberated, you may become one with Brahman.
7. Hindus worship <u>Brahman</u>.	One of the goals is to always do what is right.

Quick Activity Ancient Indian Poetry

These excerpts from Book XII of the Vedas are part of a hymn praising Prithivī, an ancient Hindu deity of the Earth. Examine the passages with a partner. Pick two and explain them in your own words in the spaces below.

1:      May she, the Queen of all that is and is to be, may Prithivī make ample space and room for us.

7:      May Earth, may Prithivī, always protected with ceaseless care by Gods who never slumber, May she pour out for us delicious nectar, may she bedew us with a flood of splendour.

8:      She who at first was water in the ocean, whom with their wondrous powers the sages [wise men] followed, May she whose heart is in the highest heaven, compassed [circled] about with truth, and everlasting, May she, this Earth, bestow upon us lustre [shininess, splendor], and grant us power in loftiest dominion [control].

18:      A vast abode [home] hast thou become, the Mighty. Great stress is on thee, press[ure] and agitation, but with unceasing care great Indra guards thee. So make us shine, O Earth, us with the splendour of gold. Let no man look on us with hatred.

44:      May Earth the Goddess, she who bears her treasure stored up in many a place, gold, gems, and riches, Giver of opulence [luxury, wealth], grant great possessions to us bestowing them with love and favour.

1.

2.

Team Challenge! **What did the Earth mean to people in ancient India as suggested by this hymn? Write a few words or phrases on a file card or slip of paper. Take turns sharing what you wrote.**

Take Notes

Literacy Skills: Compare and Contrast Use what you have read to complete the table.

Siddhartha's Life Before Enlightenment	Siddhartha's Life After Enlightenment

INTERACTIVE

For extra help, review the 21st Century Tutorial: **Compare and Contrast**.

Practice Vocabulary

Words in Context For each question below, write an answer that shows your understanding of the boldfaced key term.

1. Why is **meditation** an important part of Buddhism?

2. What happened when Buddha achieved **enlightenment**?

3. Why is it important for Buddhists to reach the goal of achieving **nirvana**?

4. Why did Buddhists live in **monasteries**?

5. What is the focus of the Buddhist sect **Theravada Buddhism**?

6. What is the focus of the Buddhist sect **Mahayana Buddhism**?

Take Notes

Literacy Skills: Analyze Cause and Effect Use what you have read to complete the table. For each cause given, write the effect.

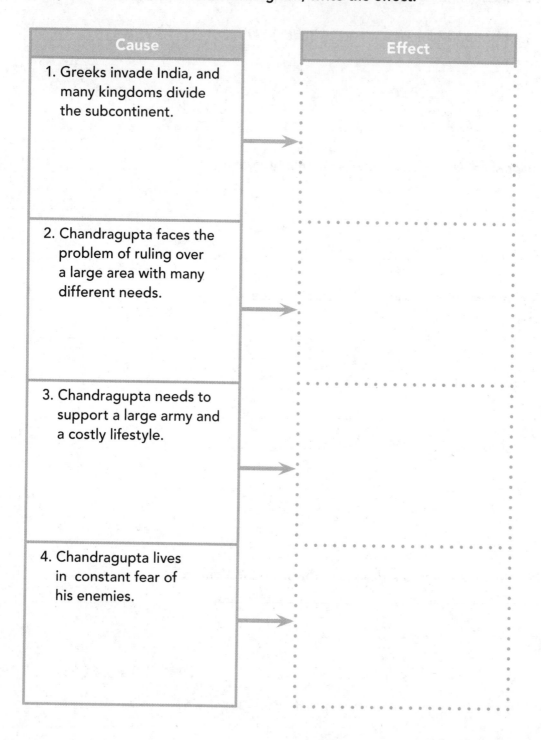

Cause	Effect
1. Greeks invade India, and many kingdoms divide the subcontinent.	
2. Chandragupta faces the problem of ruling over a large area with many different needs.	
3. Chandragupta needs to support a large army and a costly lifestyle.	
4. Chandragupta lives in constant fear of his enemies.	

👆 INTERACTIVE

For extra help, review the 21st Century Tutorial: **Analyze Cause and Effect**.

Practice Vocabulary

Sentence Revision Revise each sentence so that the underlined vocabulary word is used logically. Be sure not to change the vocabulary word. The first one is done for you.

1. As part of his <u>strategy</u>, Chandragupta attacked regions of India in no particular order.
   As part of his <u>strategy</u>, Chandragupta attacked regions of India from outside to inside.

2. Chandragupta governed each <u>province</u> by himself.

3. Chandragupta set up a <u>bureaucracy</u> so that there would be no rules or regulations.

4. Chandragupta's <u>subjects</u> spied on him.

Take Notes

Literacy Skills: Sequence Use what you have read to complete the sequence of events that led to prosperity and peace during Asoka's rule.

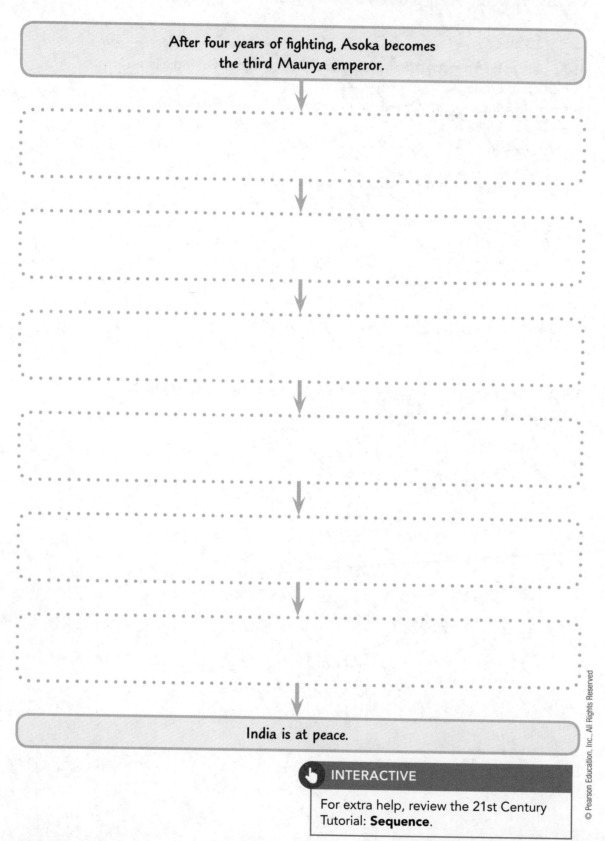

After four years of fighting, Asoka becomes the third Maurya emperor.

India is at peace.

INTERACTIVE

For extra help, review the 21st Century Tutorial: **Sequence**.

Practice Vocabulary

True or False? Decide whether each statement below is true or false. Circle T or F, and then explain your answer. Be sure to include the underlined vocabulary word in your explanation.

1. T / F A <u>stupa</u> is another word for a Buddhist monastery.

2. T / F <u>Tolerance</u> is a willingness to respect differences in beliefs and customs.

Take Notes

Literacy Skills: Summarize Use what you have read to complete the table. Fill in notes about government, culture, and achievements under the Gupta empire. Then, use your notes to write a summary of this lesson.

Government	Culture	Achievements

Summary:

INTERACTIVE

For extra help, review the 21st Century Tutorial: **Summarize**.

Practice Vocabulary

Word Map Study the word map for the word *citizenship*.
Characteristics are words or phrases that relate to the word in the
center of the word map. Non-characteristics are words and phrases
not associated with the word. Use the blank word map to explore the
meaning of the word *numeral*. Then make word maps of your own for
these words: *decimal system* and *metallurgy*.

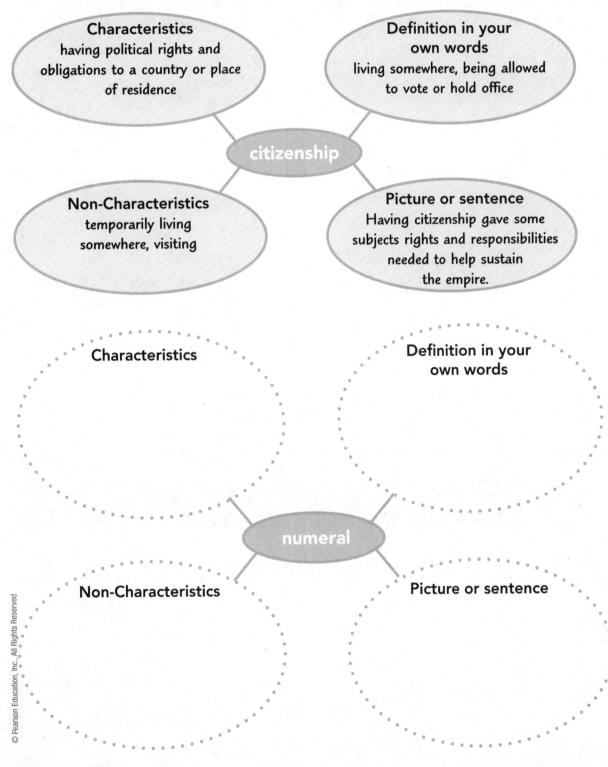

Writing Workshop Research Paper

In this topic, you will write a research paper on the technological innovations of ancient India. The prompts below will help walk you through this process.

Lessons 1 and 2 Writing Task: Generate Questions to Focus Research
(See Student Text, pages 140 and 146)

Write three to four questions about technological innovations in ancient India. Then circle the question you will focus on in your research.

Lessons 3, 4, and 5 Writing Task: Find, Use, and Cite Credible Sources
(See Student Text, pages 155, 163, and 168)

Find credible sources for your research paper on technological innovations in ancient India. Use the table below to record your notes and information about each source. Continue your list on a separate sheet of paper. Be sure to cite your sources in the format that your teacher has provided.

Sources	Notes

Lesson 6 Writing Task: Support Ideas with Evidence
(See Student Text, page 173)

Think about what you understand so far about technological innovation in ancient India. Use the spaces below to help you organize your ideas and the evidence that supports them to draw conclusions. Then write a thesis statement.

Conclusion:

Evidence:

Evidence:

Evidence:

Thesis:

Lesson 7 Writing Task: Write an Introduction (See Student Text, page 178)

Using your thesis statement and the information you have gathered, write an introductory paragraph for your research paper on a separate sheet of paper. Explain what you concluded from your research and how you are going to show it in the body of the paper.

Writing Task (See Student Text, page 181)

Using the introductory paragraph you wrote, complete your research paper discussing technological innovations in ancient India. Use transition words to clarify your ideas and make good connections between your ideas and supporting evidence found in your sources.

5 Early Civilizations of China Preview

Essential Question How do societies preserve order?

Before you begin this topic, think about the Essential Question by completing the following activity.

1. Order means a state of peace and security, free from chaos, violence, and unruly behavior. Why do you think people in your society would want to preserve order?

2. Preview the topic by skimming lesson titles, headings, and images and captions. On a sheet of paper, list features of ancient Chinese society that you believe helped preserve order.

Timeline Skills

As you read, write and/or draw at least three events from the topic. Draw a line from each event to its correct position on the timeline.

5000 BCE

2000 BCE

Map Skills

Using maps throughout the topic, label the outline map with the places listed. Then color in water, mountains, desert, and fertile river valleys.

Bay of Bengal	Chang River	East China Sea
Gobi Desert	Himalayas	Huang River
Pacific Ocean	South China Sea	Plateau of Tibet
Xi River	Yellow Sea	Shang Civilization
Zhou Civilization	Qin Dynasty	Han Dynasty

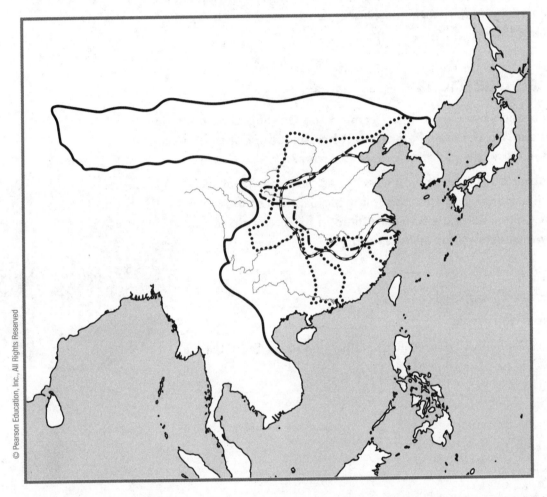

1000
BCE

1
CE

Quest
Document-Based Writing Inquiry

Evaluating a Leader's Legacy

On this Quest, you will explore primary and secondary sources about ancient China under the rule of Shi Huangdi. You will use what you learn to write an obituary, the life story of someone who has died, in which you summarize the highlights, both good and bad, of Shi Huangdi's life.

1 Ask Questions (See Student Text, page 186)

As you begin your Quest, keep in mind the Guiding Question: **How do you sum up the life of a great but harsh leader?** and the Essential Question: **How do societies preserve order?**

What other questions do you need to ask in order to answer these questions? Consider the following aspects of life in ancient China. Two questions are filled in for you. Add at least two questions for each category.

Theme Geography

Sample questions:

How did physical features in China help and hurt Shi Huangdi's ability to rule the empire?

How did Shi Huangdi modify the environment to better control the territory under his rule?

Theme Government

Theme Social Structure

Theme Economic Activity

Theme Religion and Culture

Theme My Additional Questions

 INTERACTIVE

For extra help with Step 1, review
the 21st Century Skills Tutorial:
Ask Questions.

Quest CONNECTIONS

② Investigate

As you read about ancient China, collect five connections from your text to help you answer the Guiding Question. Three connections are already chosen for you.

Connect to the Unification of China

Lesson 4 Unity Under the Qin (See Student Text, page 205)

Here's a connection! Study the infographic. How did Shi Huangdi try to standardize and centralize aspects of Chinese life? How did these methods help unify China under his rule?

What benefits and drawbacks did Shi Huangdi's efforts to create uniform standards have for China?

Connect to Orders to Burn Records

Analysis Skills Draw Sound Conclusions from Sources
(See Student Text, page 208)

Here's another connection! Read the primary source excerpt.
What orders did Shi Huangdi give to try to control history and literature
in Chinese society?

Why do you think Shi Huangdi ordered such harsh methods?

Connect to Confucian Ideals

Primary Source Confucius, *The Analects* (See Student Text, page 202)

Confucius lived and wrote his ideas before the rise of the Qin dynasty.
Read the primary source excerpt. What virtues does Confucius
suggest would be admirable in a ruler?

How did Shi Huangdi succeed or fail to live up to Confucian ideals of leadership?

Now it's your turn! **Find two more connections on your own.**
Fill in the title of your connections, then answer the questions.
Connections may be images, primary sources, maps, or text.

Your Choice | Connect to

Location in text

What is the main idea of this connection?

What does it tell you about the legacy of Shi Huangdi as a ruler?

Your Choice | Connect to

Location in text

What is the main idea of this connection?

What does it tell you about the legacy of Shi Huangdi as a ruler?

Examine the primary and secondary sources provided online or from your teacher. Fill in the chart to show how these sources provide further information about the legacy of Shi Huangdi. The first one is completed for you.

Source	Shi Huangdi's strengths and weaknesses as a ruler include . . .
Biography of Qin Shihuang	bringing harmony, order, and justice to China; standardizing tools and measurements as well as writing; laying out a clear set of laws; regulating local customs, and making waterways and dividing up the land to support farming.
Wei Liao's Report on Shi Huangdi	
Construction of the Great Wall of China	
Shi Huangdi's Tomb Complex	
The Five Confucian Classics	

👆 **INTERACTIVE**

For extra help with Step 3, review the 21st Century Skills Tutorials: **Analyze Primary and Secondary Sources** and **Analyze Images**.

④ Write an Obituary for Shi Huangdi (See Student Text, page 220)

Now it's time to put together all of the information you have gathered and use it to write an obituary for the Qin emperor Shi Huangdi.

1. **Prepare to Write** You have collected connections and explored primary and secondary sources that show the legacy of Shi Huangdi. Look through your notes and decide which achievements and shortcomings of his rule you want to include in your obituary. Record them here.

Achievements and Shortcomings of Shi Huangdi's Rule

2. **Organize Your Ideas** On a separate sheet of paper, make an outline for your obituary. List the achievements and shortcomings of Shi Huangdi's rule and put them in the order you want to discuss them. You may wish to organize your ideas in a chronological sequence or by theme, such as his impact on government and his impact on culture.

3. **Write a Draft** Using evidence from the clues you found and the documents you explored, write a draft of your obituary for Shi Huangdi. Be sure to include basic biographical information, such as when he was born and when he died. Then, describe the ways in which he affected Chinese society, good and bad. Be sure to use vivid details from the documents you've studied in this Quest.

4. **Revise Your Draft** Exchange your draft with a partner. Tell your partner what you like about his or her draft and suggest any improvements. Revise your draft based on your partner's feedback. Then, read your draft aloud. Correct any grammatical or spelling errors.

5. **Reflect on the Quest** Think about your experience completing this topic's Quest. What did you learn about ancient China under the rule of Shi Huangdi? What questions do you still have about the Qin dynasty and its society? How will you answer them?

Reflections

Take Notes

Literacy Skills: Summarize Use what you have read to complete the chart. Summarize key ideas about the geography of China and the Shang dynasty. The first one has been completed for you. Then write a summary of the lesson in the space below.

Geography of China

River Systems
China's two main rivers, the Huang and Chang, provide water for farming and movement of goods. The Huang River picks up loess and deposits it on the North China Plain when it overflows its banks. The fertile North China Plain was well-suited for agriculture and became the site of the first large settlements in China.

Isolation

The Shang Dynasty

The Shang Rise

Shang Government

Achievements

My Summary:

 INTERACTIVE

For extra help, review the 21st Century Skills Tutorial: **Summarize**.

Practice Vocabulary

Vocabulary Quiz Show Some quiz shows ask a question and expect the contestant to give the answer. In other shows, the contestant is given an answer and must supply the question. If the blank is in the Question column, write the question that would result in the answer in the Answer column. If the question is supplied, write the answer.

Question	**Answer**
1. What is a fine, dust-like material that can form soil?	1.
2.	2. dike
3. What are the earliest written records from China?	3.
4.	4. pictographs
5. What type of written character represents a complete word or phrase?	5.

Take Notes

Literacy Skills: Identify Main Idea and Details Use what you have read to complete the table. In each space write one main idea and two details. The first one has been completed for you.

Main Ideas	Supporting Details
The Zhou over-threw the Shang and started a new dynasty.	• Shang kings had become corrupt, and many Shang warriors accepted the Zhou king as their new ruler. • Zhou rulers claimed that their victory against the Shang proved that they had the support of heaven.
	•
	•
	•
	•
	•
	•
	•
	•

INTERACTIVE

For extra help, review the 21st Century Skills Tutorial: **Identify Main Ideas and Details**.

Practice Vocabulary

For each question below, write an answer that shows your understanding of the boldfaced key term.

1. How did Chinese leaders use the idea of the **Mandate of Heaven** to justify the overthrow of a dynasty?

2. How did **warlords** weaken the Zhou dynasty?

3. How did the Warring States period result in **chaos**?

Quick Activity Letter to the People

You are the ruler of the new Zhou dynasty. Officials at your court have warned that the Chinese people are fearful of your power. You need to announce to the people how and why the Zhou are now in charge. Work with a partner or in a small group to complete the letter to the people below, which will be posted throughout the empire.

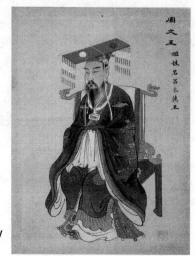

LETTER TO THE PEOPLE

I, the Zhou ruler, hereby establish a new dynasty and a new era! I hold power by right of the Mandate of Heaven.

Explain the Mandate of Heaven:

The Zhou defeated the Shang because the Shang had lost the support of heaven.

Explain which actions of the Shang caused them to lose the Mandate of Heaven:

I and my descendents will hold the Mandate of Heaven for many, many generations because we will rule wisely, and we will achieve great things.

Explain what the Zhou and you, as ruler, intend to do:

Team Challenge! Appoint a group spokesperson to read your letter aloud to the class. Discuss which letters contain the best explanations and use those to create a single class letter to post in the classroom.

Take Notes

Literacy Skills: Compare and Contrast Use what you have read to complete the table. Describe key beliefs and practices of spirit and ancestor veneration, Confucianism, and Daoism. The first one has been completed for you.

Spirit and Ancestor Veneration	Confucianism	Daoism
1. What kinds of spirits did people believe in? *good spirits and bad spirits*	1. Who founded it?	1. Who founded it?
2. Where did different spirits dwell?	2. What were its goals?	2. What were its goals?
3. Why did people honor ancestors?	3. What text contains its beliefs?	3. What text contains its beliefs?
4. How did people honor ancestors?	4. What were its core teachings?	4. What were its core teachings?

INTERACTIVE

For extra help, review the 21st Century Skills Tutorial: **Compare and Contrast**.

Practice Vocabulary

Matching Logic Using your knowledge of the underlined vocabulary words, draw a line from each sentence in Column 1 to match it with the sentence in Column 2 to which it logically belongs.

Column 1	Column 2
1. Confucianism was an important <u>philosophy</u> in ancient China.	Confucius argued that it was "the source of all virtues."
2. Confucius stressed the importance of <u>filial piety</u>.	This view of the world had a lasting impact on Chinese culture.

Quick Activity How Do Ideas Change Lives?

How did Confucianism and Daoism shape life in China? Read the quotes from Confucius and Laozi below. Work with a partner to explain each in your own words.

"The art of governing is to keep its affairs before the mind without weariness, and to practice them with undeviating consistency."

—*Confucius*

"Those who are born with the possession of knowledge are the highest class of men. Those who learn, and so readily get possession of knowledge, are the next. Those who are dull and stupid, and yet compass the learning, are another class next to these. As to those who are dull and stupid and yet do not learn; they are the lowest of the people."

—*Confucius*

"If any one desires to take the Empire in hand and govern it, I see that he will not succeed. The Empire is a divine utensil which may not be roughly handled."

—*Laozi*

"I have three precious things, which I hold fast and prize. The first is gentleness; the second is frugality; the third is humility, which keeps me from putting myself before others. Be gentle and you can be bold; be frugal, and you can be liberal; avoid putting yourself before others, and you can become a leader among men."

—*Laozi*

Team Challenge! Which philosophy do you think offered more to the ancient Chinese? Form opinion groups with those favoring the views of Confucius on one side of the room and those supporting the views of Laozi on the other. Be ready to defend your choice.

Take Notes

Literacy Skills: Use Evidence Use what you have read to complete the charts. List evidence from the lesson to support each idea. The first one has been completed for you.

Shi Huangdi unified the kingdoms of northern China and established the Qin dynasty.

He united the Warring States.	He defended the empire.	He established uniform standards.	He organized the empire.
King Zheng was skilled and ruthless and brought down rival kingdoms one by one.			

The Qin's strict laws helped forge a single nation from China's diverse regions but led to the downfall of the Qin dynasty.

The Qin government followed Legalism.	The Qin had harsh laws.	The Qin aimed for thought control.	The Qin ultimately fell from power.

👆 **INTERACTIVE**

For extra help, review the 21st Century Skills Tutorial: **Support Ideas with Evidence.**

Practice Vocabulary

Vocabulary Quiz Show Some quiz shows ask a question and expect the contestant to give the answer. In other shows, the contestant is given an answer and must supply the question. If the blank is in the Question column, write the question that would result in the answer in the Answer column. If the question is supplied, write the answer.

Question

1. ....

2. ....

3. What system of governing has strong laws and harsh punishments?

4. ....

Answer

1. Great Wall

2. standardize

3. ....

4. censor

Take Notes

Literacy Skills: Analyze Cause and Effect Use what you have read to complete the table. Record one or more effects for each cause listed. The first one has been completed for you.

Causes	Effects
To learn how to govern, Liu Bang consulted with Confucian scholars.	The new Han government followed Confucian teachings. The emperor encouraged learning and ended many harsh rules of the Qin. He lowered taxes, reduced punishments for crimes, and ended censorship.
Han emperors sought to avoid the disunity that the Zhou dynasty faced.	
Emperor Wudi wanted to find talented officials.	
Emperor Wudi needed allies to fight against the nomadic Xiongnu.	
Zhang Qian described exotic lands and horses that sweat blood.	
Han emperors made it illegal to export silk worms from China.	
The Silk Road became a path for the exchange of products and ideas.	

👆 **INTERACTIVE**

For extra help, review the 21st Century Skills Tutorial: **Analyze Cause and Effect**.

Practice Vocabulary

Sentence Builder Finish the sentences below with a key term from this section. You may have to change the form of the words to complete the sentences.

Word Bank

civil service   cuisine   envoy

official   Silk Road

1. The network of trade routes connecting China to Central Asia and Southwest Asia was known as the

2. In the Han dynasty, many layers of government existed between the villages at the bottom and the emperor at the top, and these layers included people assigned to their positions, or

3. Various types of food exchanged through trade enriched Chinese

4. Government workers who were selected based on skills and knowledge made up the

5. The Han created trade relations with kingdoms to the east by sending representatives of the emperor, known as

Take Notes

Literacy Skills: Summarize Use what you have read to complete the chart. Record important ideas from each section, and use what you have read to write a summary statement about the lesson. The first one has been completed for you.

Han Society	Economic Life	Han Achievements
The Social Order Scholars had the highest rank, followed by farmers and artisans. Below them were merchants, with slaves at the bottom.	Agriculture	China's Traditional Arts
Family Life	Industry	Advances in Science
The Role of Women	Controlling Prices and Production	Chinese Inventions

Summary Statement

INTERACTIVE

For extra help, review the 21st Century Skills Tutorial: **Summarize**.

Practice Vocabulary

Matching Logic Using your knowledge of the underlined vocabulary words, draw a line from each sentence in Column 1 to match it with the sentence in Column 2 to which it logically belongs.

Column 1	Column 2
1. Wudi turned salt mining and iron production into <u>monopolies</u>.	A metal jar dropped small balls when an earthquake was felt.
2. Among important traditional crafts practiced in the Han empire was <u>calligraphy</u>.	Artists added this hard finish to metal and wood objects.
3. Han inventors developed a <u>seismometer</u>.	The state controlled the production of these goods.
4. The Han excelled at the making of <u>lacquer</u>.	This therapy used needles to cure sickness and stop pain.
5. Han doctors began using <u>acupuncture</u> as a treatment.	Writers expressed emotion in the way that they painted Chinese characters.

Writing Workshop Arguments

As you read, build a response to this question: **Which ancient Chinese values or belief systems helped produce the most effective government in ancient China?** The prompts below will help walk you through the process.

Lesson 1 Writing Task: Introduce Claims (See Student Text, page 190)

List the values that you think made the Shang successful. Then write a sentence claiming that those values made the Shang government effective.

Lesson 2 Writing Task: Support Claims (See Student Text, page 194)

In the table, identify what values you think helped the Shang and the Zhou govern effectively, and what challenges each government faced.

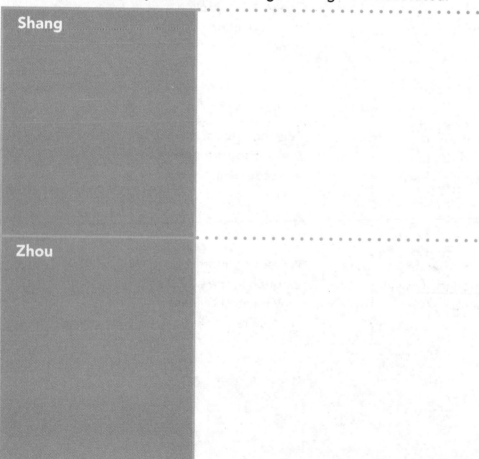

Shang	
Zhou	

Lesson 3 Writing Task: Support Claims (See Student Text, page 201)

Complete the table by describing what values from each philosophy make government more effective and how those values support your claims about the Shang and Zhou.

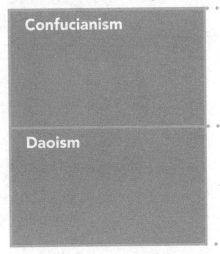

Confucianism	
Daoism	

Lesson 4 Writing Task: Use Credible Sources (See Student Text, page 207)

On a separate sheet of paper, list primary and secondary sources from the text, as well as appropriate sources from the library and the Internet, that support your claims. Consider the values that made the Qin effective, and find sources that support claims about those values. On note cards, begin taking notes and citing your sources.

Lesson 5 Writing Task: Shape Tone (See Student Text, page 213)

Consider the values or belief systems behind the success of the Han. What claims could you make about those? Now consider your claims and evidence from previous lessons. What values or belief systems were *most* effective in governing China? Draft an argument for this claim. Be sure to include at least three details from the text and from other sources to support your claim. When you finish, share your argument with a partner. Discuss whether your arguments are clear, accurate, organized, and respectful in tone. Revise your argument based on this feedback.

Lesson 6 Writing Task: Write a Conclusion (See Student Text, page 218)

To complete your argument, write one to three sentences summarizing your argument, and explaining why it matters. Write your conclusion on a separate sheet of paper.

Writing Task (See Student Text, page 221)

Using your notes, revise your draft into an argument that answers this question: Which ancient Chinese values or belief systems helped produce the most effective government in ancient China? Reread your argument and correct it for misspellings, other errors, or points of confusion. After revising it, present it to the class.

Essential Question What is the best form of government?

Before you begin this topic, think about the Essential Question by answering the following questions.

1. What are some ways in which local, state, or federal government affects your life?

2. Preview the topic by skimming lesson titles, headings, and graphics. Then place a check mark next to ancient Greek ideas or practices that you think have had the greatest influence on the modern world.

___monarchy   ___democracy

___slavery   ___colonization

Timeline Skills

As you read, write and/or draw at least three events from the topic. Draw a line from each event to its correct position on the timeline.

800 BCE	700 BCE	600 BCE

Map Skills

Using maps throughout the topic, label the outline map with the places listed. Then color in significant features of the region, such as mountains.

Europe	Asia	Greece	Aegean Sea
Ionian Sea	Mediterranean Sea	Athens	Sparta
Olympia	Troy	Peloponnesian Peninsula	Crete

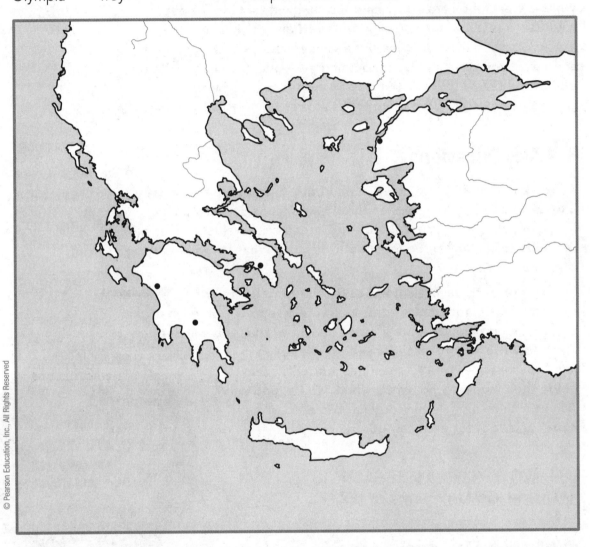

500 BCE	400 BCE	300 BCE

Quest

Project-Based Learning Inquiry

The Influence of Ancient Greece

On this Quest, you are a journalist working with a team to put together a television news magazine program on ancient Greece. You will gather information about ancient Greece by examining sources in your text and by conducting your own research. At the end of the Quest, you will write news stories, or segments, and perform a newscast presenting those stories.

 Ask Questions (See Student Text, page 226)

As you begin your Quest, keep in mind the Guiding Question: **Why has ancient Greece's culture endured?** Also, consider how ancient forms of government contributed to Greece's cultural legacy, as part of your exploration of the Essential Question: **What is the best form of government?**

For your project, each team will collect information to create a television news magazine about ancient Greece with a segment on each of the themes listed below. Create a list of questions that you will need to know to write a story on these subjects, keeping in mind the classic "Five W" questions journalists use to guide their inquiry: who, what, when, where, and why? Two questions are filled in for you. Add at least two more questions for each category.

Theme Government and Politics

Sample questions:

What kinds of government did the Greek city-states set up?

Which form of Greek government influenced many later governments, including the United States?

Theme Arts, including literature, sculpture, and architecture

Theme Science, medicine, or mathematics

Theme Sports and leisure

Theme My Additional Questions

 INTERACTIVE

For extra help with Step 1, review the 21st Century Tutorial: **Ask Questions**.

2 Investigate

As you read about ancient Greece, collect five connections
from your text to help you answer the Guiding Question.
Three connections are already chosen for you.

Connect to Athenian Democracy

Lesson 2 How did Athenian Democracy Work? (See Student Text, page 236)

Here's a connection! Look at the diagram on Athenian Democracy.
In what ways did Athenian democracy influence the government of the
United States?

What does this diagram reveal about the difference between Athenian
democracy and democracy in the United States?

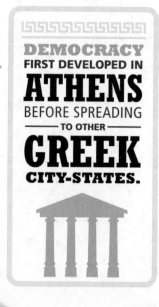

Connect to Ancient Greek Arts

Lesson 6 Arts in Ancient Greece (See Student Text, page 261)

Here is another connection! Study the photographs. What elements of order, harmony, and balance do you see in these buildings?

How has ancient Greek architecture endured in the modern age?

Connect to Greek Doctors and Scientists

Lesson 7 Science and Technology (See Student Text, page 268)

Read the information about Thales and the quote about Aristotle. How did these scientists influence how we study science today?

What role does logic and observation play in modern science?

It's Your Turn! **Find two more connections. Fill in the title of your connections, then answer the questions. Connections may be images, primary sources, maps, or text.**

Your Choice | Connect to

Location in text

What is the main idea of this connection?

What does it tell you about how ancient Greek culture has endured?

Your Choice | Connect to

Location in text

What is the main idea of this connection?

What does it tell you about how ancient Greek culture has endured?

③ Conduct Research (See Student Text, page 278)

Form teams based on your teacher's instructions. Meet to decide who will create each segment. In the chart below, record which team member will perform which task.

You will research further only the segment that you are responsible for. Use the ideas in the connections to further explore the subject you have been assigned. Pick who or what you will report about, and find more sources about that subject.

Be sure to find valid sources and take good notes so you can properly cite your sources. Record key information about your story's subject and brainstorm ways to enhance your points with visuals.

Team member	Segment	Specific Topic of Segment
	Philosophy and religion	
	Government and politics	
	Arts, including literature, sculpture, and architecture	
	Science, medicine, or mathematics	
	Sports and leisure	

👆 INTERACTIVE

For extra help, review the 21st Century Tutorials: **Work in Teams, Search for Information on the Internet,** and **Avoid Plagiarism**.

4 Create Your News Magazine (See Student Text, page 278)

Now it's time to put together all of the information you have gathered and write your segment.

1. **Prepare to Write** Review the research you've collected, and make sure the information you've gathered really supports the main point of your segment.

The main point of your piece:

Key information to support that point:

Sources to cite:

Possible visual/visuals to support your main point:

2. **Write a Draft** The segment should be about three minutes long, which is about one to one-and-one-half pages of single-spaced typed text. This means you will have to be brief and get straight to the point.

3. **Share with a Partner** Once you have finished your draft, ask one of your team members to read, or listen to you read, your draft and provide comments on the clarity and flow of the information. Revise the segment based on his or her comments, and comment on his or her segment, if possible.

4. **Create a Visual** Now that you have the text of your segment, find or create a visual to support your key points. This will give your viewers something to look at while you are delivering your segment.

5. **Put Together Your News Magazine** Once all the team members have written and revised their segments, it's time to put them together. You can do this in a couple of ways: 1) by recording each segment using a phone or video camera and editing them together; or 2) by performing the news magazine for the class live. Your teacher will let you know her/his preference for delivery. Either way, you should rehearse the newscast beforehand, taking care to write smooth transitions from one segment to the next.

6. **Perform Your News Magazine** Show or perform your news magazine for the class. View the other teams' news magazines, and take notes on the information they shared.

Notes on other news magazines:

7. **Reflect** After all the presentations, discuss your thoughts on your news magazine and the other news magazines. Reflect on the project, and list what you might do differently next time so the teamwork goes more smoothly.

Reflections

 INTERACTIVE

For extra help, review the 21st Century Tutorial: **Give an Effective Presentation**.

Take Notes

Literacy Skills: Analyze Cause and Effect Use what you have read to complete the organizer. For each event, write the cause in the box to the left and the effect in the box to the right. The first one has been completed for you.

Cause	Event	Effect
The mountains of Greece were too steep and rocky for farming.	People settled in the lowland valleys and plains.	The mountains isolate these lowland settlers, who develop independent communities.
	The Greeks become skillful sailors and merchants.	
	Mycenaean civilization is destroyed.	
	In the 700s BCE, the Greeks develop an alphabet.	

👆 **INTERACTIVE**

For extra help, review the 21st Century Tutorial: **Analyze Cause and Effect**.

Practice Vocabulary

Vocabulary Quiz Show Some quiz shows ask a question and expect the contestant to give the answer. In other shows, the contestant is given an answer and must supply the question. If the blank is in the Question column, write the question that would result in the answer in the Answer column. If the question is supplied, write the answer.

Question

1.

2.

3. Where were temples and public buildings located in Greek city-states?

4. What did the Greeks call the art and practice of government?

5. What term means "rule by the best people"?

Answer

1. polis

2. citizens

3.

4.

5.

Take Notes

Literacy Skills: Summarize Use what you have read to complete the flowcharts. Write a summary for each set of facts. The first flowchart has been completed for you.

Summary: Great Political Variety Existed Among City-States.

Tyrants came to power in some Greek cities, while oligarchs ruled other cities.	First Athens, and then other Greek cities, developed democracy.

Summary:

The reforms of Solon and Cleisthenes increased the number of citizens who could vote.	Pericles' reforms allowed citizens to be paid for jury service and other civic duties.

Summary:

The population of Athens was small.	Not all the people who lived in Athens were citizens.

INTERACTIVE

For extra help, review the 21st Century Tutorial: **Summarize**.

Practice Vocabulary

Sentence Builder Finish the sentences below with a key term from this section. You may have to change the form of the words to complete the sentences.

Word Bank

oligarchy   phalanx   representative democracy

democracy   citizenship   direct democracy

tyranny

1. Many city-states moved toward rule by the many, a form of government called

2. Membership in a community in which people help make government decisions is called

3. A political system in which citizens elect others to represent them in government is called a(n)

4. Political power is held by a small group of people in a(n)

5. A political system in which citizens participate directly in decision-making is called a(n)

6. A formation of heavily armed foot soldiers who moved together as a unit was called a(n)

7. Government run by a strong ruler is known as

Take Notes

Literacy Skills: Compare and Contrast Use what you have read to complete the graphic organizers. For each category, compare and contrast Sparta and Athens. The first organizer has been done for you.

Government	
Sparta	**Athens**
A mix of monarchy, oligarchy, and democracy	Democracy

Economy	
Sparta	**Athens**

Culture and the Arts	
Sparta	**Athens**

INTERACTIVE

For extra help, review the 21st Century Tutorial: **Compare and Contrast**.

Practice Vocabulary

Words in Context For each question below, write an answer that shows your understanding of the boldfaced key term.

1. How did **ephors** give the Spartan assembly an important power?

2. How were **helots** different from slaves?

3. Why did Sparta become a **military state**?

4. Why did Spartan males live in **barracks**?

Quick Activity Contrasting Primary Sources

With a partner or small group, contrast these two primary sources to answer the question: What were the differences in point of view and perspective between Athenians and Spartans?

[Lycurgus, law-maker of the Spartans] believed motherhood to be the most important function of freeborn woman. Therefore, in the first place, he insisted on physical training for the female no less than for the male sex: moreover, he instituted races and trials of strength for women competitors as for men, believing that if both parents are strong they produce more vigorous offspring. . . .

Lycurgus, on the contrary, instead of leaving each father to appoint a slave to act as tutor, gave the duty of controlling the boys to a member of the class from which the highest offices are filled, in fact to the "Warden" as he is called. He gave this person authority to gather the boys together, to take charge of them and to punish them severely in case of misconduct. He also assigned to him a staff of youths provided with whips to chastise them when necessary; and the result is that modesty and obedience are inseparable companions at Sparta.

— From Xenophon's *Constitution of the Lacedaimonians*, translated by E.C. Marchant and G.W. Bowersock, Chapter 1

"If we turn to our [the Athenians'] military policy, there also we differ from our antagonists. We throw open our city to the world, and never by alien acts exclude foreigners from any opportunity of learning and observing, although the eyes of an enemy may occasionally profit by our liberality; trusting less in system and policy than to the native spirit of our citizens; while in education, where our rivals from their very cradles by a painful discipline seek after manliness, at Athens we live exactly as we please, and yet are just as ready to encounter every legitimate danger."

— From Pericles' *Funeral Oration from the Peloponnesian War,* in *The History of the Peloponnesian War,* Thucydides, Book 2

Team Challenge! For each primary source, write out a statement of the author's perspective on education. Then, find a partner and discuss education in ancient Greece, with one of you taking the Spartan point of view and the other the Athenian point of view.

Take Notes

Literacy Skills: Use Evidence Use what you have read to complete the table. On each row, provide either evidence or a conclusion, based on your reading of the text. The first row has been done for you.

Evidence	Conclusion
Spartan women could sell property; they were educated and trained in sports.	In contrast to the women of other city-states, Spartan women had more freedom.
	The economy of all the city-states depended on slavery.
Greek colonies spread across the Mediterranean Sea and the Black Sea.	
Most Greek women were expected to remain indoors, managing the home, while men conducted business outside the home.	

INTERACTIVE

For extra help, review the 21st Century Tutorial: **Support Ideas With Evidence**.

Practice Vocabulary

Word Map Study the word map for the word *tenant farmer*. Characteristics are words or phrases that relate to the word in the center of the word map. Non-characteristics are words and phrases not associated with the word. Use the blank word map to explore the meaning of the word *metic*. Then make a word map of your own for the word *slavery*.

Characteristics
poorer than small farmers and aristocrats
paid rent in either money or crops

Definition in your own words
farmers who did not own land but paid rent to grow crops on another person's land

tenant farmer

Non-characteristics
rich, great landowner
raised livestock
produced a food surplus

Picture or sentence
The tenant farmer paid rent to the landowner.

Characteristics

Definition in your own words

metic

Non-characteristics

Picture or sentence

Take Notes

Literacy Skills: Compare and Contrast Use what you have read to complete the tables. For each battle or war, compare and contrast the advantages and/or disadvantages of each side in the conflict. The first table has been done for you.

Battle of Marathon	
Persians	**Athenians**
Outnumbered the Athenians by about two to one	Unlike the Persians, had no archers or cavalry, but won the battle because they relied on surprise

Second Persian War	
Persians	**Greeks**

Peloponnesian War	
Spartans	**Athenians**

INTERACTIVE

For extra help, review the 21st Century Tutorial: **Compare and Contrast**.

Practice Vocabulary

Words in Context For each question below, write an answer that shows your understanding of the boldfaced key term.

1. What happened at the **Battle of Salamis**?

2. What was the **Delian League**, and why was it formed?

3. Who made up the **Peloponnesian League**, and why did its members resent Athens?

4. Why was the **Battle of Marathon** significant?

Take Notes

Literacy Skills: Synthesize Visual Information Use what you have read and the images in the lesson to complete the graphic organizers. For each visual, find a passage in the text that will allow you to combine the visual and the information in the text in order to create a fuller picture, or synthesis. The first graphic organizer has been done for you.

Photograph of the Discus Thrower Found in the Text	Information Found in the Text
The figure looks proud and heroic, like an "ideal." The fact that a sculptor chose an athlete as a subject shows that the Greeks admired athletes.	The text says, "The most famous sports event was the Olympic games, which honored Zeus. These games took place every four years. During the games, all conflicts between city-states ceased."

Synthesis: The Greeks believed that sports were among the most important things in life and even pleased the gods.

Table of Oympian Gods Found in the Text	Information Found in the Text

Synthesis:

INTERACTIVE

For extra help, review the 21st Century Tutorial: **Synthesize**.

Practice Vocabulary

Vocabulary Quiz Show Some quiz shows ask a question and expect the contestant to give the answer. In other shows, the contestant is given an answer and must supply the question. If the blank is in the Question column, write the question that would result in the answer in the Answer column. If the question is supplied, write the answer.

Question	Answer
1. What is the worship of many gods called?	1.
2.	2. mythology
3. Which famous sports event took place every four years and honored Zeus?	3.
4.	4. lyric poetry
5.	5. chorus

Quick Activity Create a Comic Strip

Hundreds of fables from ancient Greece are said to have been written by Aesop, an enslaved person who was given his freedom because of his wisdom and talent. Although Aesop was likely not a real person, the fables said to be written by him have endured for hundreds of years. Read this text from one of Aesop's Fables.

The Fox and the Crow

A crow, having stolen a bit of flesh, perched in a tree and held it in her beak. A Fox, seeing this, longed to possess himself of the flesh, and by a wily stratagem succeeded.

"How handsome is the Crow," he exclaimed, "in the beauty of her shape and in the fairness of her complexion! Oh, if her voice were only equal to her beauty, she would deservedly be considered the Queen of Birds!"

This he said deceitfully; but the Crow, anxious to [respond to the criticism of] her voice, set up a loud caw and dropped the flesh.

The Fox quickly picked it up, and thus addressed the Crow: "My good Crow, your voice is right enough, but your wit is wanting."

— From *Three Hundred Aesop's Fables,* translated by George Fyler Townsend

Team Challenge! Form teams to create a comic strip that illustrates the story. Use speech bubbles to have the characters talk to one another.

Take Notes

Literacy Skills: Summarize Use what you have read to complete the flowcharts. Write a summary for each set of facts. The first flowchart has been completed for you.

Summary: The Greeks valued the human power of reason to help people understand their lives and world.

By asking questions, Socrates encouraged people to think more clearly.

Plato wrote about the nature of reality.

Summary:

Thucydides hoped that his history of the Peloponnesian War would help people avoid repeating the mistakes of the past.

The historian Xenophon believed that the study of history could teach people how to live moral lives.

Summary:

Through observation, the Greeks realized that natural laws governed the universe.

The philosopher Aristotle sought knowledge through observation. He was a great collector and classifier of data.

INTERACTIVE

For extra help, review the 21st Century Tutorial: **Summarize**.

Practice Vocabulary

Sentence Builder Finish the sentences below with a key term from this section. You may have to change the form of the words to complete the sentences.

Word Bank

Academy   hypothesis

Hippocratic oath   Socratic method

1. A question-and-answer method of teaching is called the

2. Plato's famous school of philosophy was called the

3. After making observations of a natural event, Greek scholars explained their observations by forming a logical guess called a(n)

4. When promising to use their knowledge only in ethical ways, doctors state the

Take Notes

Literacy Skills: Sequence Use what you have read to complete the flowcharts in order to show the sequence of events. The first flowchart has been completed for you.

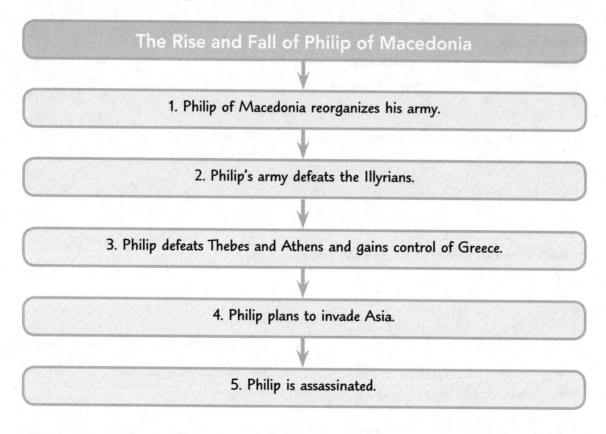

The Rise and Fall of Philip of Macedonia

1. Philip of Macedonia reorganizes his army.

2. Philip's army defeats the Illyrians.

3. Philip defeats Thebes and Athens and gains control of Greece.

4. Philip plans to invade Asia.

5. Philip is assassinated.

The Rise and Fall of Alexander the Great
1. Alexander crushes revolts and burns Thebes.
2.
3.
4. In Egypt, Alexander founds the city of Alexandria.
5.
6.
7. Alexander dies in 323 BCE.

INTERACTIVE

For extra help, review the 21st Century Tutorial: **Sequence**.

Practice Vocabulary

Use a Word Bank Choose one word from the word bank to fill in each blank. When you have finished, you will have a short summary of important ideas from the section.

Word Bank

sarissa   Hellenistic   classical civilization

Philip of Macedonia gained control of Greece with powerful, disciplined troops, each of whom was armed with a ....

After Philip was assassinated, his son Alexander gained the throne.

Alexander secured control of Greece and then captured cities in Asia and along the Mediterranean coast. He freed Egypt from the Persians and founded Alexandria on the Nile delta. After defeating the Persian empire, Alexander moved east into India. Alexander founded Greek-style cities from which emerged .... culture.

Alexander's conquests helped spread Greek culture. In time, Greek and Roman culture would form ....

Writing Workshop Explanatory Essay

As you read, build a response to this question: **Why did the power of the independent Greek city-states rise, peak, and fall?** Use examples from this topic to support your main points. The prompts below will help walk you through the process.

Lesson 1 Writing Task: Consider Your Purpose (See Student Text, page 232)

What is your purpose in writing this essay? Who is your audience?

Lesson 2 Writing Task: Pick an Organizing Strategy
(See Student Text, page 237)

Choose an organization strategy that lends itself to the type of explanation you are giving. Sometimes, the phrasing of the writing prompt can provide a clue to what type of organization to choose. In this case, the question in the writing prompt starts with "Why?" Here are some common organizational strategies. Check off the one you think will work best for this writing prompt:

__definition   __classification
__compare/contrast   __cause/effect

Lessons 3 and 5 Writing Task: Develop a Clear Thesis and Update Your Thesis (See Student Text, pages 243 and 255)

Now, express in one sentence the main point you want to make in your essay. From what you've read so far, why did the power of the independent Greek city-states rise, peak, and fall? Update your thesis as you continue to read through the lessons.

Lessons 4 and 6 Writing Task: Support Thesis with Details
(See Student Text, pages 249 and 262)

Begin to organize your essay with an outline showing the string of causes you are explaining. Record supporting details in this outline as you read.

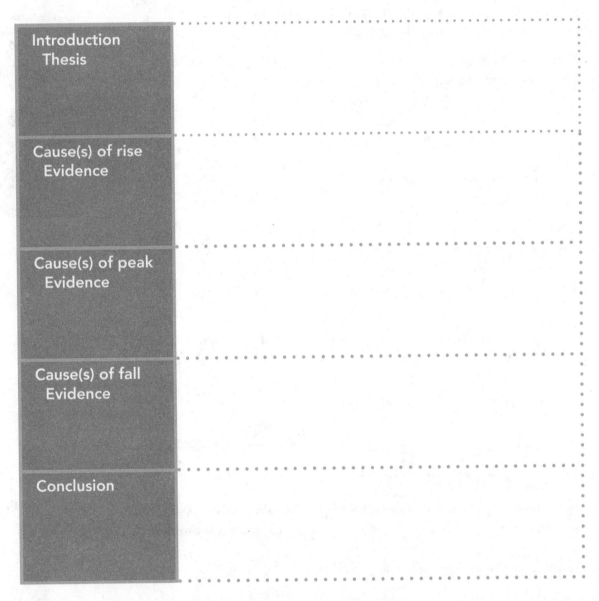

| Introduction Thesis |
| Cause(s) of rise Evidence |
| Cause(s) of peak Evidence |
| Cause(s) of fall Evidence |
| Conclusion |

Lesson 7 Writing Task: Draft Your Essay (See Student Text, page 270)

Using the outline you created, answer the following question in a five-paragraph explanatory essay: Why did the power of the independent Greek city-states rise, peak, and fall?

Lesson 8 Writing Task: Revise Your Essay (See Student Text, page 277)

Read your draft. Ask yourself: Have I made my point clearly? Is it supported by enough evidence? Exchange drafts with a partner and use their feedback to revise your essay.

TOPIC 7

The Roman Republic Preview

Essential Question What is the best form of government?

Before you begin this topic, think about the Essential Question by completing the following activity.

1. List five jobs, or purposes, for government. In a small group, discuss why you think these jobs are important.

2. What forms of government do you think might best fulfill these jobs? Place a check mark next to three of the forms listed. Circle the one that you think is the best form of government.

___democracy   ___dictatorship   ___republic

___monarchy   ___aristocracy   ___oligarchy

Timeline Skills

As you read, write and/or draw at least three events from the topic. Draw a line from each event to its correct position on the timeline.

900 BCE	700 BCE	500 BCE

Map Skills

Using maps throughout the topic, label the outline map with the places listed. Then use different colors for areas ruled by the Roman republic in 44 BCE, 146 BCE, 264 BCE, and 500 BCE. Create a map key to define what each color symbolizes.

Po River	Mediterranean Sea	Tiber River	Alps
Rome	Carthage	Athens	Italy
Greece	Sicily	Gaul	Byzantium

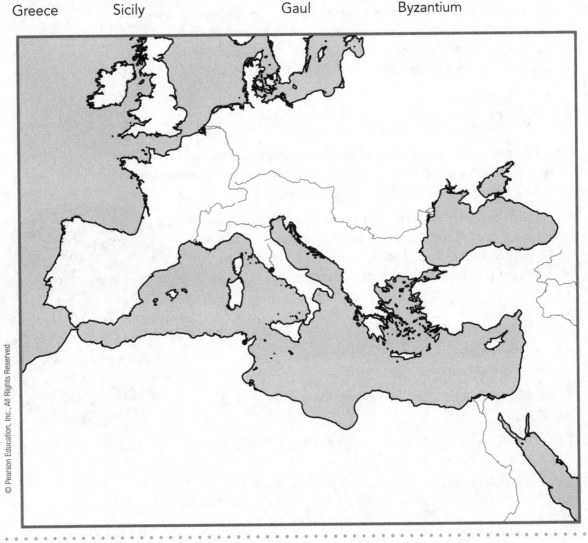

| 300 BCE | | 100 BCE |

Quest

Document-Based Writing Inquiry

The Roman Influence

On this Quest, you need to find out how Rome influenced later governments. You will examine sources about the Roman republic and later governments to find similarities. At the end of the Quest you will write an explanatory essay describing the long-term influence of the Roman republic.

1 Ask Questions (See Student Text, page 284)

As you begin your Quest, keep in mind the Guiding Question: **How did Rome's government influence later governments?** and the Essential Question: **What is the best form of government?**

What other questions do you need to ask in order to answer these questions? Consider the following aspects of life in the Roman republic. Two questions are filled in for you. Add at least two questions for each category.

Theme Formation of the Republic

Sample questions:

How did a republic form among the first people to settle in Rome?

What factors contributed to the rise of the republic?

Theme Roman Security, Military Power, and Expansion

Theme Structure, Principles, and Powers of the Roman Republic

Theme Social Hierarchy and Religion under the Roman Republic

Theme Decline and Legacy of the Roman Republic

Theme My Additional Questions

👆 **INTERACTIVE**

For extra help with Step 1, review the 21st Century Skills Tutorial: **Ask Questions**.

2 Investigate

As you read about the Roman republic, collect five connections from your text to help you answer the Guiding Question. Three connections are already chosen for you.

Connect to Founding the Republic

Lesson 1 Rome Becomes a Republic (See Student Text, page 288)

Here's a connection! What qualities does a republic have? Where did the name *republic* come from?

How did the nature of the Roman republic's government resemble that of the United States today?

Connect to Branches of Government

Lesson 2 Three Branches of Roman Government (See Student Text, page 292)

Here's another connection! Study the infographic. How did the Roman republic balance power among its three branches of government? How did this structure provide for a separation of powers, and checks and balances?

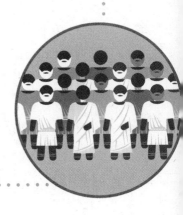

What influence do you think the branches of government in the Roman republic had on modern democracies?

Connect to Cicero, *The Republic*

Lesson 4 In-text Primary Source *The Republic* (See Student Text, page 305)

Read the in-text Primary Source excerpt from Marcus Tullius Cicero's *The Republic.* How is what Cicero describes similar to or different from the ways in which people try to influence government in the United States today?

What role did the senate play in Rome's governance? What influence do you think the Roman republic had on modern democracies?

Now it's your turn! Find two more connections on your own. Fill in the title of your connections, then answer the questions. Connections may be images, primary sources, maps, or text.

Your Choice | Connect to

Location in the text

What is the main idea of this connection?

What does it tell you about the ways the Roman republic influenced modern democracies, such as that of the United States?

Your Choice | Connect to

Location in the text

What is the main idea of this connection?

What does it tell you about the ways the Roman republic influenced modern democracies, such as that of the United States?

3 Examine Primary and Secondary Sources

(See Student Text, page 309)

Examine the primary and secondary sources provided online or from your teacher. Fill in the chart to show how these sources provide further information about how the Roman republic influenced later governments. The first one is completed for you.

Sources	Ways the Roman Republic Influenced Later Governments
Preamble to the U.S. Constitution	Government should serve the public welfare, establish the rule of law in a constitution, and derive its power from the people.
Law of the Twelve Tables	
Separation of Powers in Practice	
U.S. Capitol Building and Roman Pantheon	
The Founders of the United States' Classical Education	

> **INTERACTIVE**
>
> For extra help with Step 3, review the 21st Century Skills Tutorial: **Analyze Images**.

4 Write Your Explanatory Essay (See Student Text, page 309)

Now it's time to put together all of the information you have gathered and use it to write your explanatory essay.

1. **Prepare to Write** You have collected connections and explored sources that show how the government of the Roman republic influenced future governments. Look through your notes and decide which lasting influences of the Roman republic you want to highlight in your essay. Record them here.

Lasting Influences

2. **Write a Draft** Using evidence from the connections you found and the documents you explored, write a draft of your explanatory essay. Introduce your thesis in response to the Guiding Question: How did Rome's government influence later governments? Then, in the body of your essay, support your thesis by describing three or more lasting influences of the Roman republic, citing evidence from the documents you've studied in this Quest. Finally, summarize your explanation with memorable insight in the concluding paragraph of your essay.

3. **Share with a Partner** Exchange your draft with a partner. Tell your partner what you like about his or her draft and suggest any improvements.

4. **Finalize Your Essay** Revise your draft based on your partner's feedback. Then, read aloud your essay. Correct any grammatical or spelling errors.

5. **Reflect on the Quest** Think about your experience completing this topic's Quest. What did you learn about the Roman republic and its legacy? What benefits and drawbacks did a republican form of government have for ancient Rome? How has your study of this topic affected your understanding of and opinions about the government of our country today?

Reflections

🖑 INTERACTIVE

For extra help with Step 4, review the 21st Century Skills Tutorial: **Write an Essay**.

Take Notes

Literacy Skills: Analyze Cause and Effect Use what you have read to complete the chart. In each space, write ways in which geography and previous cultures affected the Roman republic. The first effect has been started for you.

Cause	Effects
Geography	• Less rugged terrain, including large, flat plains, made it easy for soldiers to travel and unite the country. • • •
Greek Culture	• • • •
Etruscan Culture	• • • •

INTERACTIVE

For extra help, review the 21st Century Skills Tutorial: **Analyze Cause and Effect**.

Practice Vocabulary

Words in Context **For each question below, write an answer that shows your understanding of the boldfaced key term.**

1. What activities most likely took place in the **forum** of ancient Rome?

2. How did Rome's government change when the **republic** replaced the monarchy?

3. What advantages did a **maniple** give Romans in battle?

4. Approximately how many soldiers made up a **legion**? What kind of soldiers were they?

Take Notes

Literacy Skills: Identify Main Idea and Details Use what you have read to complete the concept web. In each space, write details that support the main idea. The first one has been completed for you.

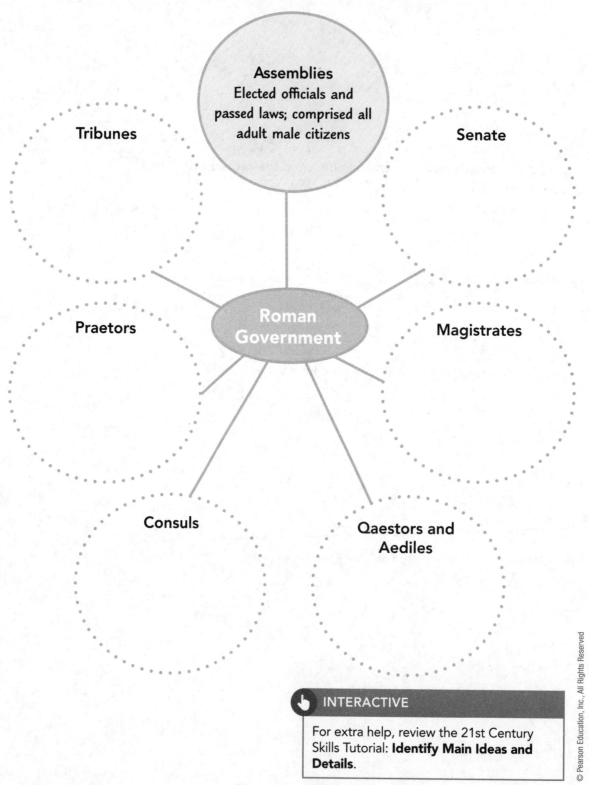

Assemblies
Elected officials and passed laws; comprised all adult male citizens

Tribunes

Senate

Praetors

Roman Government

Magistrates

Consuls

Qaestors and Aediles

👆 **INTERACTIVE**

For extra help, review the 21st Century Skills Tutorial: **Identify Main Ideas and Details**.

Practice Vocabulary

Vocabulary Quiz Show Some quiz shows ask a question and expect the contestant to give the answer. In other shows, the contestant is given an answer and must supply the question. If the blank is in the Question column, write the question that would result in the answer in the Answer column. If the question is supplied, write the answer.

Question

1. What do you call the highest officials in the Roman republic?

2.

3. What power could certain Roman officials use to stop or cancel the actions of other officials?

4.

5. What garment worn by adult male citizens of Rome symbolized their citizenship?

Answer

1.

2. constitution

3.

4. magistrates

5.

Quick Activity Explore Roman Numerals

Between 900 BCE and 800 BCE, Roman numerals appeared. Historians believe that ancient Romans developed their numerals from earlier Etruscan numerals. They used these numerals to track time, goods, money, and even people. Roman numerals appear on many ancient texts and artifacts.

Arabic Numerals	Roman Numerals	Arabic Numerals	Roman Numerals
1	I	9	IX
2	II	10	X
3	III	50	L
4	IV	100	C
5	V	200	CC
6	VI	500	D
7	VII	1000	M
8	VIII		

Roman numbers are based on seven basic numerals combined according to certain rules:

1. Add the total of the numbers shown to determine the amount: XXV = 25 (10 + 10 + 5)

2. Arrange numbers from largest at left to smallest at the right.

3. You may repeat I, X, C, and M in a single number.

4. Do not repeat more than 3 of the same numeral in a row, instead put a I to the left of a larger number: IV = 4; IX = 9; XIX = 19 and so on.

Write these Roman numbers in Arabic numbers. Follow the rules above.

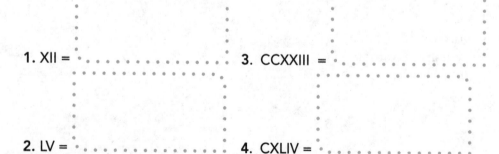

1. XII =

2. LV =

3. CCXXIII =

4. CXLIV =

Team Challenge! Write a few sets of Roman numbers. Switch with a partner to have them write the number in Arabic numerals.

Take Notes

Literacy Skills: Classify and Categorize Use what you have read to complete the chart. In each space, list the people of the Roman republic who belonged to this social group. Then, describe one aspect of life for this social group.

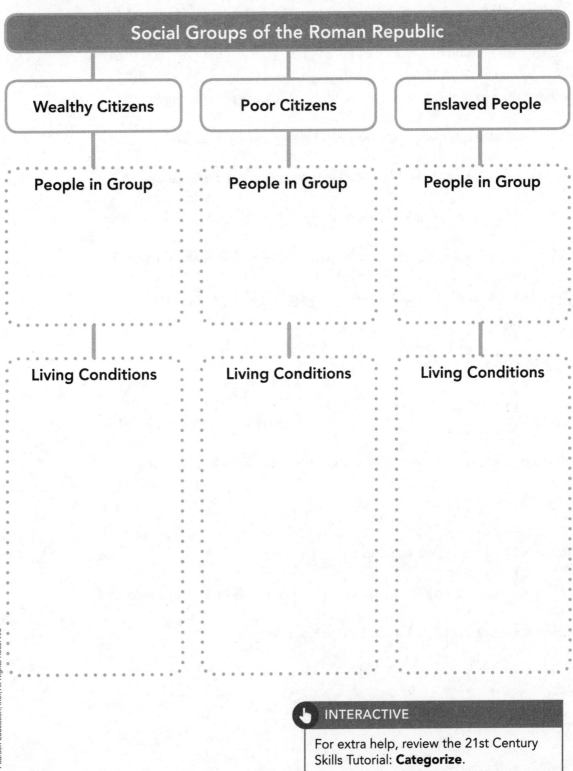

Social Groups of the Roman Republic

Wealthy Citizens	Poor Citizens	Enslaved People
People in Group	**People in Group**	**People in Group**
Living Conditions	**Living Conditions**	**Living Conditions**

INTERACTIVE

For extra help, review the 21st Century Skills Tutorial: **Categorize**.

Practice Vocabulary

Use a Word Bank Choose one word from the word bank to fill in each blank. When you have finished, you will have a short summary of important ideas from the section.

Word Bank

patriarchal society   villas

established religion   paterfamilias

Life for Roman families varied according to the part of society in which

they lived. Most Romans were poor, and many were slaves. These

common people had hard lives filled with hard work and difficult living

conditions. A few Romans were wealthy and lived in great comfort. Their

city homes had beautiful courtyards, gardens, and even running water.

These families sometimes traveled to the countryside to enjoy their

....
.   .
.   .
....

Regardless of class, Roman families were led by the oldest man in the

family. A .... had total power over the family.

He owned all the property and made all the decisions. A society that

organizes power this way is called a ....

Romans of all classes also shared an ...., one

that was supported by the government. For this reason, Romans held the

government responsible for keeping the gods happy.

Quick Activity How Does Roman Society Compare?

Ancient civilizations had distinct social systems that, in their own way, preserved order and provided structure. Study the two civilizations shown in the pyramids. What do you notice about their social systems? Discuss your ideas with a partner, and write down three similarities and three differences that you observe.

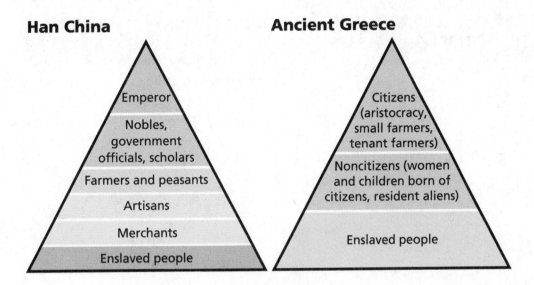

Han China

- Emperor
- Nobles, government officials, scholars
- Farmers and peasants
- Artisans
- Merchants
- Enslaved people

Ancient Greece

- Citizens (aristocracy, small farmers, tenant farmers)
- Noncitizens (women and children born of citizens, resident aliens)
- Enslaved people

Roman Republic

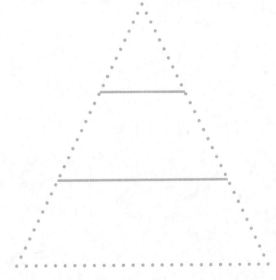

Team Challenge! How do these social systems compare with that of the Roman republic? Use what you have learned to fill in the pyramid for Rome's hierarchy. In small groups, discuss the similarities and differences that you noted between the Han China and Ancient Greece hierarchies. Then, try to think of three similarities and three differences between Roman society and some other societies. Finally, take a class vote: Which two civilizations had the most similar social systems? Which had the most different? Discuss your findings.

Take Notes

Literacy Skills: Summarize Use what you have read to complete the chart. In the box at the left, explain the weaknesses of the Roman republic. In the box at the right, describe the actions of those responsible for the Roman republic's crisis. Then, summarize the effects of those problems during the republic's final crisis.

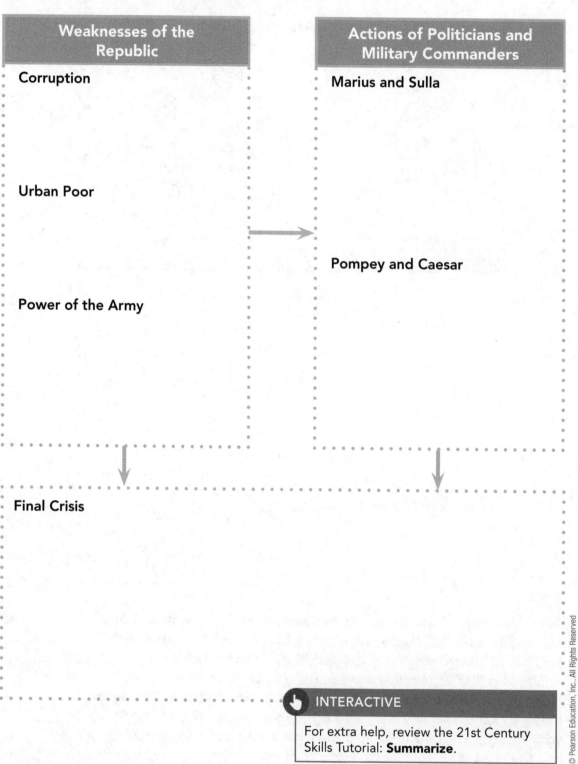

Weaknesses of the Republic

Corruption

Urban Poor

Power of the Army

Actions of Politicians and Military Commanders

Marius and Sulla

Pompey and Caesar

Final Crisis

INTERACTIVE

For extra help, review the 21st Century Skills Tutorial: **Summarize**.

Practice Vocabulary

Word Map Study the word map for the word *province*. Characteristics are words or phrases that relate to the word in the center of the word map. Non-characteristics are words and phrases not associated with the word. Use the blank word map to explore the meaning of the term *civil war*. Then make word maps of your own for these words: *empire* and *Augustus*.

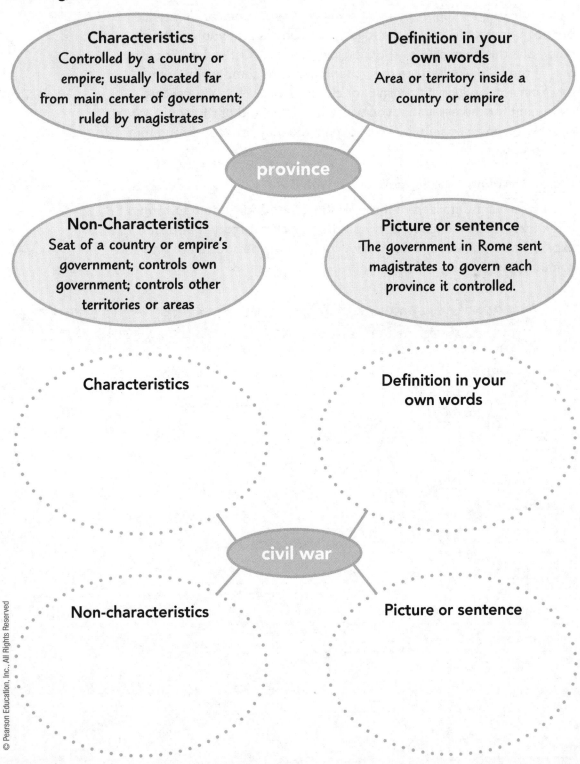

Characteristics
Controlled by a country or empire; usually located far from main center of government; ruled by magistrates

Definition in your own words
Area or territory inside a country or empire

province

Non-Characteristics
Seat of a country or empire's government; controls own government; controls other territories or areas

Picture or sentence
The government in Rome sent magistrates to govern each province it controlled.

Characteristics

Definition in your own words

civil war

Non-characteristics

Picture or sentence

Writing Workshop Research Paper

As you read, build a response to this question: **How does Rome compare to an earlier or contemporary society in terms of environment, political system, citizenship, or cultural connection?** The prompts below will help walk you through the process.

Lesson 1 Writing Task: Develop a Clear Thesis (See Student Text, page 289)

Express in one sentence the most significant similarities or differences between Rome and one of the following societies that you've already studied in this course: Greek, Hellenistic, Chinese, or Persian. Choose one of the following factors to further focus your comparison on: environment, politics, citizenship, or culture. This will be your thesis statement for the essay that you will write at the end of this topic. Write your thesis on a separate piece of paper. You may revise it throughout the workshop.

Lesson 2 Writing Task: Support Thesis with Details (See Student Text, page 296)

Gather relevant details from these lessons. Categorize them to form three main ideas. Choose two details from each category that best explain each main idea. If necessary, consult outside sources to find and confirm details. Fill in the table below.

	Key Details (two for each Main Idea)	Supporting outside sources (if needed)
Main Idea 1:		
Main Idea 2:		
Main Idea 3:		

Lessons 3 and 4 Writing Task: Draft Your Essay and Write a Conclusion

(See Student Text, page 300 and 306)

Fill in the outline with key words and phrases to express your plan for your essay. Develop your thesis into an introductory paragraph, and develop your three main ideas and six details into three body paragraphs. Refine your conclusion to reflect any new thoughts and connections that emerge as you write.

I. Introduction:

    A. Thesis:

    B. Main Idea 1:

    C. Main Idea 2:

    D. Main Idea 3:

    E. Introduction Conclusion:

II. Main Idea 1:

    A. Detail:

    B. Detail:

    C. Paragraph Conclusion:

III. Main Idea 2:

    A. Detail:

    B. Detail:

    C. Paragraph Conclusion:

IV. Main Idea 3:

    A. Detail:

    B. Detail:

    C. Paragraph Conclusion:

V. Conclusion Paragraph

Writing Task (See Student Text, page 310)

Exchange essay drafts with a partner. Read and provide feedback on your partner's draft, and invite feedback on your draft. Do your drafts provide a clear thesis statement that answers the question: **How does Rome compare to an earlier or contemporary society in terms of environment, political system, citizenship, or cultural connection?** Do your drafts have appropriate supporting details? Address these questions, and make revisions to your draft as needed.

Essential Question What forces can cause a society to change?

Before you begin this topic, think about the Essential Question by answering the following question.

1. What are some ways that your community has changed over time? List three ways in which you have seen people, businesses, and other elements of society change.

Timeline Skills

As you read, write and/or draw at least three events from the topic. Draw a line from each event to its correct position on the timeline.

250 BCE	1 CE	250 CE

Map Skills

Using maps throughout the topic, label the outline map with the places listed. Then, color in the territory ruled by the Roman empire.

Byzantium	Rome	Jerusalem	Mediterranean Sea
Black Sea	Rhine River	Danube River	Anatolia
Egypt	Greece	Gaul	Spain

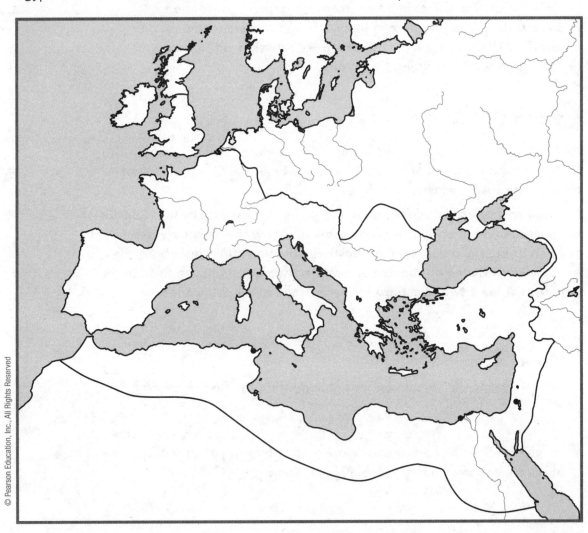

500 CE	1000 CE	1250 CE	1500 CE

Quest
Discussion Inquiry

The Fall of Rome

On this Quest, you will explore sources and gather information about the decline of the Roman empire from the perspective of a historian. Then, you will participate in a discussion with other historians about the Guiding Question.

1 Ask Questions (See Student Text, page 314)

As you begin your Quest, keep in mind the Guiding Question: **Could the fall of Rome have been prevented?** and the Essential Question: **What forces can cause a society to change?**

The Roman empire lasted for about 450 years, but eventually fell. Consider the events that led up to the fall of Rome and how the themes listed may have contributed to the fall. List questions that you might ask about the effect of each theme on the Roman empire. Two questions are filled in for you. Add at least two questions for each of the other categories.

Theme Economic Weakness

How were trade routes affected by fighting within the Roman empire?

If people within the Roman empire could not afford to pay their taxes, how did that affect the emperor's ability to maintain an army?

Theme Political Conflict

Theme Political Corruption

Theme Social Conflict

Theme Invasions from Outside

Theme My Additional Questions

 INTERACTIVE

For extra help with Step 1, review the
21st Century Skills Tutorial: **Ask Questions**.

2 Investigate

As you read about the decline of the Roman empire, collect five connections from your text to answer the Guiding Question. Three connections are already chosen for you.

Connect to Augustus

Primary Source Augustus, *The Deeds of the Divine Augustus*
(See Student Text, page 322)

Here's a connection! Consider the list of great deeds that Augustus wrote about himself. What evidence can you find that Augustus was concerned about maintaining the strength of the empire?

Considering he was one of the greatest of Rome's emperors, why do you think Augustus found it necessary to write a long list of the things he had done?

Connect to Satire and Biography

Lesson 4 In-text Primary Source Juvenal's *Satire 10* (See Student Text, page 341)

What does this connection tell you about what Roman citizens were thinking about during times of trouble?

How do you think the Roman citizenry's attitude toward the government affected the empire's stability?

Connect to Economic Problems Worsen

Lesson 5 What was the Imperial Crisis? (See Student Text, page 346)

Here's another connection! Read the description of inflation in your text. What does the description tell you about the value of the Roman coins over time?

What does that indicate about what was happening to the Roman economy?

It's Your Turn! **Find two more connections. Fill in the title of your connections, then answer the questions. Connections may be images, primary sources, maps, or text.**

Your Choice | Connect to

Location in text

What is the main idea of this connection?

What does it tell you about the decline of the Roman empire? Could it have been prevented?

Your Choice | Connect to

Location in text

What is the main idea of this connection?

What does it tell you about the decline of the Roman empire? Could it have been prevented?

3 Examine Sources (See Student Text, page 362)

Examine the secondary sources provided online or from your teacher. Fill in the chart to note the viewpoints of four historians on the question of whether Rome's fall could have been prevented. The first one is completed for you.

Could the fall of Rome have been prevented?	
Source	**Yes or No? Why?**
The Decline and Fall of the Roman Empire	NO, because the empire was too big to support.
The Day of the Barbarians	
History of the Later Roman Empire	
The Fall of the Roman Empire	

👆 **INTERACTIVE**

For extra help with Step 3, review the 21st Century Skills Tutorial: **Compare Viewpoints.**

4 Discuss! (See Student Text, page 362)

Now that you have collected connections and explored documents about the fall of the Roman empire, you are ready to discuss with your fellow historians the Guiding Question: **Could the fall of Rome have been prevented?** Follow the steps below, using the spaces provided to prepare for your discussion.

You will work with a partner in a small group of historians. Try to reach consensus, a situation in which everyone is in agreement, on the question. Can you do it?

1. **Prepare Your Arguments** You will be assigned a position on the question, either YES or NO.

    My position:

    Work with your partner to review your Quest notes from the Quest Connections and Quest Sources.

    - If you were assigned YES, agree with your partner on what you think were the strongest arguments from Bury and Grant.

    - If you were assigned NO, agree on what you think were the strongest arguments from Gibbon and Barbero.

2. **Present Your Position** Those assigned YES will present their arguments and evidence first. As you listen, ask clarifying questions to gain information and understanding.

What is a Clarifying Question?	
These types of questions do not judge the person talking. They are only for the listener to be clear on what he or she is hearing.	
Example: Can you tell me more about that?	Example: You said [x]. Am I getting that right?

 INTERACTIVE

For extra help with Step 4, review the 21st Century Skills Tutorial: **Participate in a Discussion or Debate**.

While the opposite side speaks, take notes on what you hear in
the space below.

3. **Switch!** Now NO and YES will switch sides. If you argued YES before,
   now you will argue NO. Work with your same partner and use your notes.
   Add any arguments and evidence from the clues and sources. Those *now*
   arguing YES go first.

   When both sides have finished, answer the following:

Before I started this discussion with my fellow historians, my opinion was that	*After* I started this discussion with my fellow historians, my opinion was that
_____the fall of Rome could have been prevented. _____the fall of Rome could not have been prevented.	_____the fall of Rome could have been prevented. _____the fall of Rome could not have been prevented.

4. **Point of View** Do you all agree on the answer to the Guiding Question?

   ____ Yes

   ____ No

   If not, on what points do you all agree?

Take Notes

Literacy Skills: Analyze Cause and Effect Use what you have read to complete the table. Factors that helped the Roman empire grow appear in the left column. Record ways that those factors contributed to the empire's growth in the right column. One has been completed for you.

Causes	Effects
Rule by emperors	ended civil wars; brought peace; made the empire more stable for a time; began the Pax Romana
Pax Romana	
Rome's practical achievements	
Roman military	
Roman trade and economic activity	

👆 **INTERACTIVE**

For extra help, review the 21st Century Skills Tutorial: **Analyze Cause and Effect**.

Practice Vocabulary

Sentence Builder Finish the sentences below with a vocabulary term from this section. You may have to change the form of the words to complete the sentences.

Word Bank

aqueduct   concrete

deify   Pax Romana

1. Emperors who are officially declared to be gods have been

2. Romans experienced a long period of peace and prosperity during the

3. Mixing stone and sand with limestone, clay, and water produces a useful building material called

4. Roman cities grew rapidly, partly because engineers brought water great distances through

Quick Activity Where Do They Go Next?

The Roman Empire reached its greatest territorial extent under Emperor Trajan who ruled from 98 CE to 117 CE. With a partner, study the map of the Roman empire and what surrounded its borders in 117 CE.

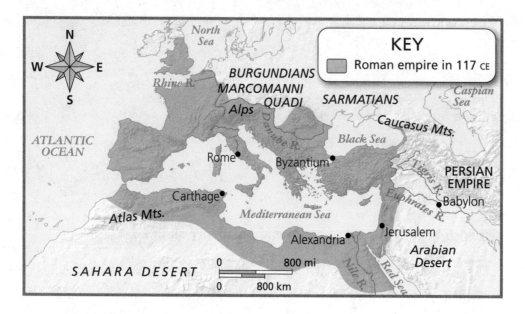

Team Challenge! You probably noticed that the Roman Empire expanded across a large area of southern Europe, North Africa, and parts of southwestern Asia. What lands were left to conquer? Where could the Romans go next? What physical features, peoples, or empires lie at the empire's northern, southern, eastern, and western borders? Form a group with three other students. In your group, answer the question: Why did the Roman empire fail to expand after 117 CE? Write your responses on a post-it note, and add them to the class board.

Take Notes

Literacy Skills: Sequence Use what you have read to complete the timeline. Record what happened on each of the dates listed. Then connect each box to the timeline at the appropriate spot. One has been completed for you.

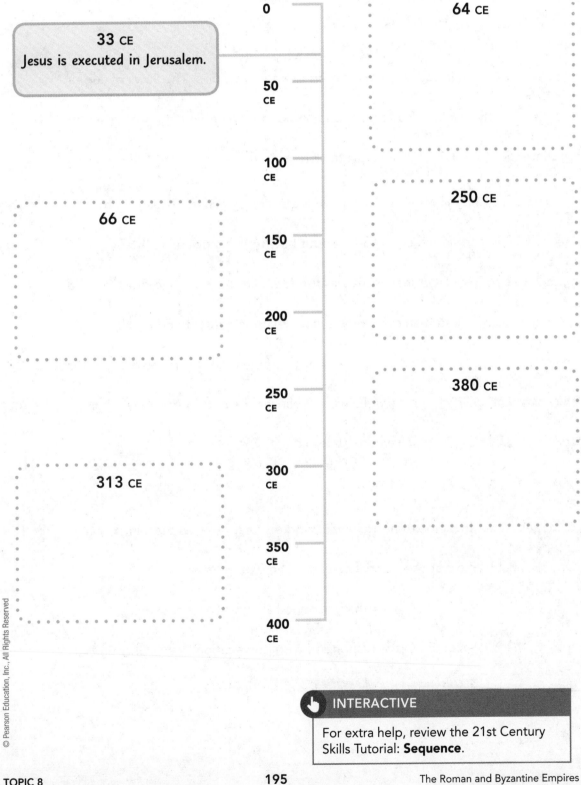

33 CE
Jesus is executed in Jerusalem.

64 CE

66 CE

250 CE

313 CE

380 CE

0

50 CE

100 CE

150 CE

200 CE

250 CE

300 CE

350 CE

400 CE

INTERACTIVE

For extra help, review the 21st Century Skills Tutorial: **Sequence**.

Practice Vocabulary

Word Bank Choose one word from the word bank to fill in each blank. When you have finished, you will have a short summary of important ideas from the section.

Word Bank

baptism   conversion   crucifixion

martyr   resurrection

Christianity began in Judea, then part of the Roman empire. The Jews of Judea

practiced many religious traditions, including a ritual plunging into water, which

was later adopted by Christianity as the rite of _____.

According to Christian tradition, Jesus of Nazareth preached ideas from the

Hebrew Bible and added other ideas about how to live a good life. Many

people began to believe that Jesus was the Messiah. As more and more people

followed Jesus, the Roman government saw Jesus as a threat and had him

executed by _____. Some of Jesus' followers said that

they saw him again after his death. These believers helped form a new religion

called Christianity. They believed that Jesus' _____

was proof that he was the Messiah.

After Jesus' death, some of his followers worked to spread his teachings.

One was Paul, who opposed Christianity until he experienced a

_____ that changed his views. As Christianity

spread, many Roman emperors responded with persecution. Many Christians

died for their beliefs. A person who dies for his or her beliefs is called a

_____.

The Roman and Byzantine Empires

Take Notes

Literacy Skills: Analyze Text Structure Use what you have read to complete the outline. The items listed below reflect the headings and subheadings in the lesson. Record key details beneath the headings. The first one has been completed for you.

I. The Christian Bible
    A. The Old and New Testaments
        1. The Old Testament comprises the scriptures of the Hebrew Bible.
        2. The New Testament comprises 27 documents, called *books*, added by Christians.
    B. What Are the Gospels?

    C. Teachings in Other Books

II. What Do Christians Believe About God?
    A. The Son of God

    B. The Soul and Salvation

    C. The Trinity

III. Practicing Christianity
    A. Following Jesus' Teachings

    B. Christianity Today

    C. Christian Rituals and Holidays

IV. What Is the Judeo-Christian tradition?

 INTERACTIVE

For extra help, review the 21st Century Skills Tutorial: **Organize Your Ideas**.

Practice Vocabulary

Vocabulary Quiz Show Some quiz shows ask a question and expect the contestant to give the answer. In other shows, the contestant is given an answer and must supply the question. If the blank is in the Question column, write the question that would result in the answer in the Answer column. If the question is supplied, write the answer.

Question

1. What text makes up the second part of the Christian Bible, and is not part of the Hebrew Bible?

2. _____

3. _____

4. What stories did Jesus often use to teach important lessons?

5. What are large groups within Christianity that share certain beliefs and rituals, but disagree on others?

6. _____

7. What subject deals with issues of right and wrong and the best way to treat people?

Answer

1. _____

2. epistles

3. Trinity

4. _____

5. _____

6. Gospel

7. _____

Take Notes

Literacy Skills: Identify Main Ideas and Details Use what you have read to complete the concept web. Record details about each aspect of Roman culture under the empire. The first one has been completed for you.

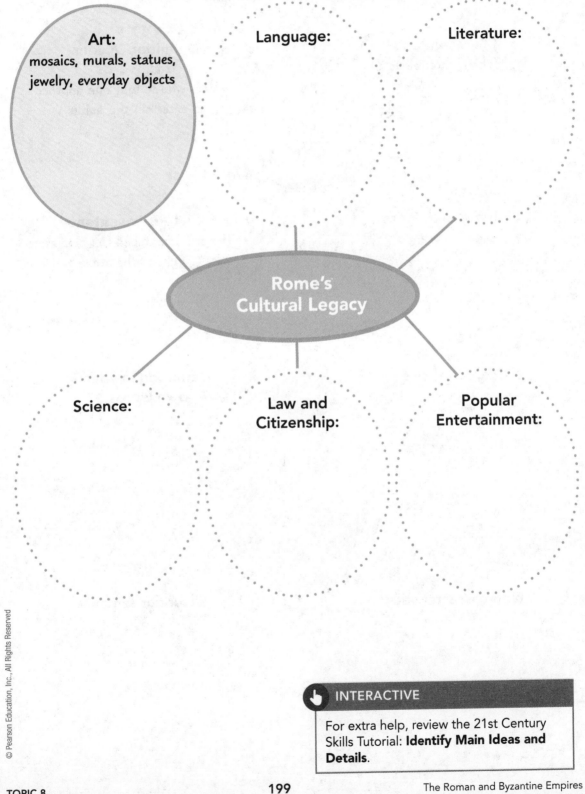

Art:
mosaics, murals, statues, jewelry, everyday objects

Language:

Literature:

Rome's Cultural Legacy

Science:

Law and Citizenship:

Popular Entertainment:

> **INTERACTIVE**
>
> For extra help, review the 21st Century Skills Tutorial: **Identify Main Ideas and Details**.

Practice Vocabulary

Word Map Study the word map for the word *gladiator*. Characteristics are words or phrases that relate to the word in the center of the word map. Non-characteristics are words and phrases not associated with the word. Use the blank word map to explore the meaning of the word *oratory*. Then make word maps of your own for these words: *site of encounter, mosaic, Romance languages, Greco-Roman,* and *satire.*

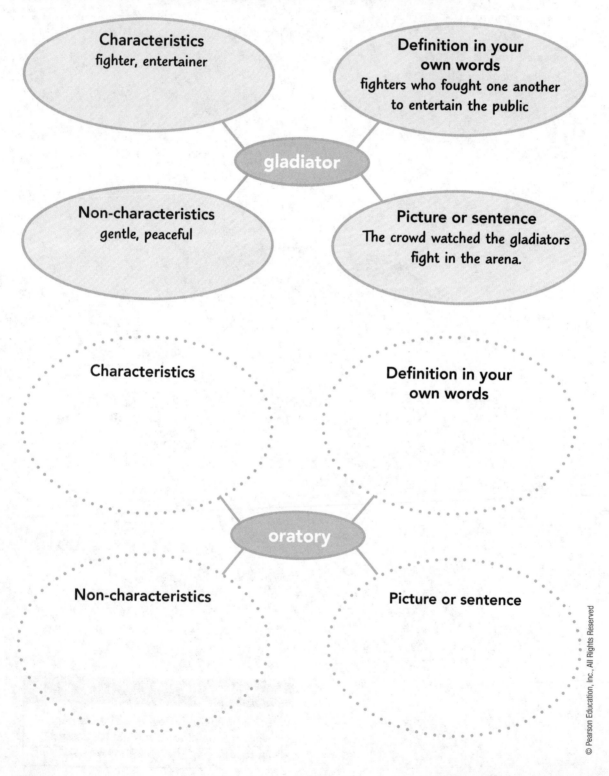

Characteristics
fighter, entertainer

Definition in your own words
fighters who fought one another to entertain the public

gladiator

Non-characteristics
gentle, peaceful

Picture or sentence
The crowd watched the gladiators fight in the arena.

Characteristics

Definition in your own words

oratory

Non-characteristics

Picture or sentence

Take Notes

Literacy Skills: Analyze Cause and Effect Use what you have read to complete the chart. Record specific events and their effects that contributed to the decline of the Roman empire.

Cause	Event	Effect
Marcus Aurelius dies.		Pax Romana ends.
Civil wars erupt.	Inflation grows. Trade networks are disrupted. Foreign invasions advance.	
Diocletian tries to stabilize Rome.		Military leaders fight for power.
Theodosius dies.		Rome falls.

INTERACTIVE

For extra help, review the 21st Century Skills Tutorial: **Analyze Cause and Effect**.

Practice Vocabulary

Words in Context For each question below, write an answer that shows your understanding of the **boldfaced** key term.

1. What are problems that people might have in a time of **inflation**?

2. According to the Romans, why were the Germans **barbarians**?

3. How did Emperor Theodosius show his support for Christian **orthodoxy**?

4. What role did **mercenaries** play in the Roman empire's fight to survive?

Quick Activity Did the Roman Empire Fall?

Read the excerpt below. Discuss with a partner what the excerpt suggests about the "fall" of the western Roman empire.

> "Nations innumerable and most savage have invaded all Gaul. The Whole region between the Alps and the Pyrenees, the ocean and the Rhine, has been devastated … Oh wretched Empire! … Who could believe that Rome, built upon the conquest of the whole world, would fall to the ground?"
>
> —*St. Jerome on the Germanic Invasions, 409 C.E.*

In 476 CE, Germanic invaders overthrew the last Roman emperor in the western empire, Romulus. The city of Rome fell. Meanwhile, to the east, the Byzantine empire continued and even thrived. Not until 1453 did the Ottoman Turks capture the Byzantine capital of Constantinople. Historians often refer to the end of the western Roman empire as the "fall" of the Roman empire. Some argue that the empire did not fall, however. They maintain that the empire broke down slowly, over a long period of time, and that Roman civilization continued in the east as the Byzantine empire, up until 1453. Use what you have learned in the lessons to discuss, in a small group, the causes of the decline of the western Roman empire as well as the ways in which Roman civilization continued.

Team Challenge! Take a Thumb Vote in response to the question **Did the Roman empire fall?** Organize into groups based on your votes. With your new group, write a paragraph that answers the question and provides at least two pieces of evidence to support your position. If you answer "yes," explain why *fall* is an appropriate description, despite suggestions that Roman civilization continued beyond 476 CE. If you answer "no," explain why *fall* is wrong and suggest an alternative word or phrase as a more appropriate description.

Take Notes

Literacy Skills: Use Evidence Use what you have read to complete the table. Record the main idea for each heading in the lesson. Then, list evidence to support the main idea. The first one has been completed for you.

Main Idea	Evidence
What Was the New Rome? The Eastern Roman, or Byzantine, empire grew around a new political and economic center.	• Constantine established the capital of the Eastern Roman empire at Constantinople, on the site of Byzantium. • Located on the Bosporous Strait, Constantinople became a center for trade and was easier to defend than Rome.
Who Were Justinian and Theodora?	• •
The Shrinking Empire	• •
The Empire's Influence	• •
Early Russia	• •

Practice Vocabulary

Sentence Revision Revise each sentence so that the underlined vocabulary word is used logically. Be sure not to change the vocabulary word. The first one is done for you.

1. The <u>Byzantine</u> empire was named after Emperor Constantine.
   The <u>Byzantine</u> empire was so named because its capital, Constantinople, was built at a place once called Byzantium.

2. A <u>strait</u> is a wide body of water surrounding an island.

3. The <u>moat</u> was a trench filled with stones.

4. <u>Greek fire</u> was a liquid that quickly stopped flames from spreading.

5. A <u>missionary</u> generally lacked the confidence to promote his religion.

6. The <u>Cyrillic alphabet</u> was used by the Romans.

Take Notes

Literacy Skills: Compare and Contrast Use what you have read to complete the chart. List features that the Roman Catholic Church and the Eastern Orthodox Church share, as well as features that make each church unique. One has been completed for you.

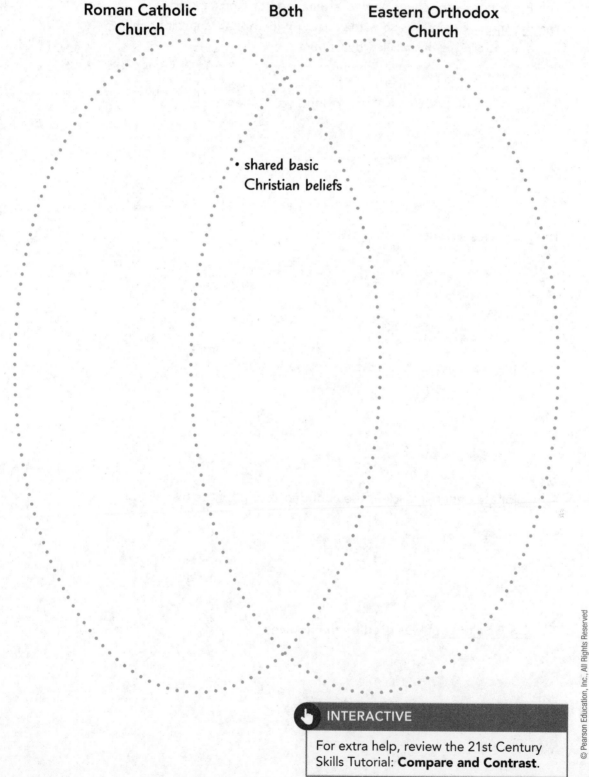

Roman Catholic Church   Both   Eastern Orthodox Church

- shared basic Christian beliefs

INTERACTIVE

For extra help, review the 21st Century Skills Tutorial: **Compare and Contrast**.

Practice Vocabulary

Sentence Builder Finish the sentences below with a key term from this section. You may have to change the form of the words to complete the sentences.

Word Bank

creed   Great Schism   icon

iconoclast   Justinian's Code   pope

1. Church leadership was the most important issue between Eastern Orthodox and Roman Catholic churches in the

   ....
   .   .
   .   .
   .   .
   ....

2. The leader of the Roman Catholic church was the

   ....
   .   .
   .   .
   .   .
   ....

3. Many Christians believed it was wrong to worship holy images called

   ....
   .   .
   .   .
   .   .
   ....

4. The Byzantine empire and its emperor benefited from the unified body of law organized under

   ....
   .   .
   .   .
   .   .
   ....

5. In 325, Church officials prepared a clear statement of beliefs, or

   ....
   .   .
   .   .
   .   .
   ....

6. Byzantines who destroyed holy images in churches were called

   ....
   .   .
   .   .
   .   .
   ....

Writing Workshop Arguments

As you read, build a response to this question: Which civilization was greater, the Greek city-states or the Roman empire? The prompts below will help walk you through the process.

Lessons 1 and 2 Writing Tasks: Introduce Claims and Gather Details
In this topic, you will write an argument on the question: Which was greater, the Greek city-states or the Roman empire? Consider the following factors: size, longevity, economic power, cultural achievements, and influence. Add facts about each civilization to this chart.

Factor	Greece	Rome	Advantage? (G/R)
Size			
Longevity			
Economic power			
Culture Achievements			

Lesson 3 Writing Task: Use Credible Sources On a separate sheet of paper, list at least three print or digital sources, other than your text, that you will use to check your conclusions.

Lesson 4 Writing Task: Introduce a Claim Look at your chart and mark which civilization had the advantage in each area in your opinion. From this exercise, can you choose which civilization you think was greater? If you can't support choosing one, argue that they both have claims to greatness. Form your conclusion into a one-sentence statement and write it in the outline.

Lessons 5 and 6 Writing Tasks: Support a Claim and Distinguish Claims from Opposing Claims Make an outline of your essay, listing your best examples of why one society might be greater than the other and an opposing claim.

Claim statement	
2nd best example	
3rd best example	
Opposing claim	
Best example	

Lesson 7 Writing Task: Shape Tone As your write, use phrases such as "clearly" or "in fact," to emphasize your points and phrases such as "on the other hand," or "in contrast" to introduce an opposing claim.

Writing Task Using the outline you created, answer the following question in a five-paragraph argument: Which was greater, the Greek city-states or the Roman empire?

 INTERACTIVE

For extra help, review the 21st Century Skills Tutorials: **Support Ideas with Evidence** and **Consider and Counter Opposing Arguments**.

Acknowledgments

Photography

002: World History Archive/Alamy Stock Photo; **004:** E&E Image Library Heritage Images/Newscom; **005:** Will Steeley/Alamy Stock Photo; **006:** The Irish Image Collection/Design Pics Inc/Alamy Stock Photo; **007:** Debu55y/Fotolia; **009:** Clement Philippe/Arterra Picture Library/Alamy Stock Photo; **010:** Zev Radovan/BibleLandPictures/Alamy Stock Photo; **011:** Ann Ronan Picture Library Heritage Images/Newscom; **018T:** Pierre Andrieu/Staff/AFP/Getty Images; **018B:** Mike Greenslade/Alamy Stock Photo; **021:** Ancient Art & Architecture Collection Ltd/Alamy Stock Photo; **030:** Interfoto/Personalities/Alamy Stock Photo; **031:** Image Asset Management/World History Archive/Age Fotostock; **032:** Photo Researchers, Inc/Alamy Stock Photo; **033:** Pictures From History/The Image Works; **056:** Peter Horree/Alamy Stock Photo; **059:** Michael DeFreitas Middle East/Alamy Stock Photo; **061:** Akg Images/Franois Gunet/Newscom; **063:** David Keith Jones/Images of Africa Photobank/Alamy Stock Photo; **064:** Sylvain Grandadam/Age Fotostock; **065:** Efesenko/Fotolia; **068B:** Stuart Gleave/Moment Open/Getty Images; **068T:** Santiago Urquijo/Moment Open/Getty Images; **071B:** A wall painting at Beni Hasan depicting the moving of a colossal statue of a Pharaoh (colour litho), Cailliaud, Frederic (1787–1869) (after)/Private Collection/The Stapleton Collection/Bridgeman Images; **071T:** Fatih Kocyildir/Shutterstock; **076:** Roger Bacon/Reuters/Alamy Stock Photo; **078:** Twinsterphoto/Fotolia; **079:** Godong/Alamy Stock Photo;

081: M.A.Pushpa Kumara/EPA/Newscom; **083:** Saiko3p/iStock/Getty Images; **088BL:** Peter Horree/Alamy Stock Photo; **088BR:** Robert Harding Productions/Alamy Stock Photo; **088TL:** World History Archive/Alamy Stock Photo; **088TR:** CM Dixon/Heritage Image Partnership Ltd/Alamy Stock Photo; **104:** Weerapong Pumpradit/Shutterstock; **106:** Paul Springett 10/Alamy Stock Photo; **107:** Snark/Art Resource, NY; **108:** Danita Delimont/Gallo Images/Getty Images; **109:** Zhuhe2343603/Shutterstock; **111:** BL/Robana/Robana Picture Library/Age Fotostock; **113:** Hung Chung Chih/Shutterstock; **118:** BnF, Dist. RMN-Grand Palais/Art Resource, NY; **130:** Zack Frank/Fotolia; **132:** Erich Lessing/Art Resource,NY; **135:** Fine Art Images/Heritage Image Partnership Ltd/Alamy Stock Photo; **137:** Richard Osbourne/Alamy Stock Photo; **138:** Anatoly Vartanov/Fotolia; **160:** Nito/Shutterstock; **162:** Atlaspix/Alamy Stock Photo; **163:** Cliff Owen/AP Images; **167:** alessandro0770/123RF; **168:** Dmitry Naumov/123RF; **169:** World History Archive/Alamy Stock Photo; **182:** Peter Horree/Alamy Stock Photo; **185:** Akg Images/Newscom; **186:** David Ball/Alamy Stock Photo; **187:** Interfoto/Personalities/Alamy Stock Photo; **189:** Erich Lessing/Art Resource,NY;

Text

Harvard University Press Xenophon in Seven Volumes by E. C. Marchant and G. W. Bowersock. Copyright © Harvard University Press 1925.